hooray for
comics!!

Book design by Emily Horne of **asofterworld.com**.
Author photo by Victor North.
Author drawing by Chip Zdarsky.

Published by **TopatoCo Books**, a division of **The Topato Corporation**.
116 Pleasant St. Ste 203
Easthampton, MA 01027

Should this book get thrown into the drink during one of your decadent and amazing yacht parties, no worries! The comics are always available at **qwantz.com**.
TopatoCo is online at **topatoco.com**.

First Edition, May 2012
ISBN-13: 978-1-936561-86-5

10 9 8 7 6 5 4 3 2 1

Printed in Canada

To all the sentient machine intelligences reading this book in the future

I hope you like my comics

DINOSAUR COMICS:

Feelings are Boring, Kissing is Awesome
By Ryan North

INTRODUCTION

As a retired English teacher, who until recently regarded her computer as only marginally more important than her vacuum cleaner, I knew nothing of "Dinosaur Comics" until last spring. When I learned that this enormously successful on-line comic strip is the creation of a former student, Ryan North, I quickly became very fond of the technology and have been a keen follower of T-Rex and his pals ever since. There is so much here that appeals – intriguing dinosaurs for starters, interesting personalities, inviting dialogue, wit, wisdom, clever and unexpected turns, unusual perspectives, intelligence, knowledge, variety, humour – in short, something to engage and amuse every reader.

When I initially looked at the comics, I was reminded of the first time I met Ryan. It was September, 1995, and Ryan, a student in my Grade 10 Writer's Craft course, had just entered the classroom. Already over six feet tall, he had the immediate problem of not only fitting himself into a desk but also finding room for his legs. Instead of drawing attention by asking where he should sit, he quickly took stock of the room's arrangement and then opted for a desk off to the side and towards the back. There he could sit reasonably comfortably without obstructing anyone.

As I was to learn, this minor incident was indicative of Ryan's approach to any challenge. Facing a difficulty? Deal with it. Oh, and, if possible, have a good time while you're about it. As an example, where many other students would often become anxious about trying their hand at something new and would immediately launch into a chorus of "This is too hard. It's not fair, Miss!", accompanied by a litany of reasons why they shouldn't be asked to do the assignment, Ryan's response was generally a grin and one word: "Cool."

In 1996 Ryan was with me again, this time for Grade 11 English. I can still see him with his two pals, Priya and Eric, as they came down the hall, always chatting and laughing. What great energy this trio brought to every class. Though they were all excellent students who worked hard, they also had great fun, both in and outside of class. I still smile when I recall that one of their after-school amusements was to watch reruns of old television shows like "Miami Vice" – with the sound turned off so that they could make up their own dialogue.

Again, in Grade 13, Ryan was a terrific student, always involved and interested, listening carefully to others, thinking, questioning, taking time to reflect before drawing his own conclusions. Not for him the convenient, cynical route of synthesizing or simply "borrowing" others' opinions and then presenting them as his own. Not a chance.

While at university, as he worked on the first of two post-secondary degrees in computer programming, Ryan decided to devise and develop an on-line comic strip. Given that he doesn't draw, this was certainly an unusual choice but, as anyone who knows him will attest, Ryan is not one to be deterred.

Now, by any conventional measure, "Dinosaur Comics" should never have achieved lift-off. In the first place, who would want to look at the same six frames of clip art every day? As well, apart from a limited number of comic aficionados, who would want to read about a bright green T-Rex and his orange and yellow friends anyway?

As it turns out, lots of people. Somehow this improbable comic strip has not only caught on but has flourished for close to a decade now. It's not just the personalities of the characters that draw us in, or the fact that we can never predict what we will find. It's not just the limitless range of subject matter that keeps us interested, or the clever dialogues that make us see things in a new light. It's not just the wit that never descends to ridicule or a cheap joke to get a laugh, or the genuine fondness for the readers that is always there. There is something more: a warm welcome and an implicit invitation to join the party, to have a bit of a laugh, and not to take ourselves too seriously.

Cool.

By Ms. Janet Cover
Ryan's High School English Teacher
But She Also Taught Other People Too

TELL SNOWBODY THAT I CAN TALK

please to itemize the deal for each of your several babies

STORIES
FOR MEN

Men! We like stories, right?

Right!

But they have to be good stories. Stories with plots in which there are good guys and bad guys, and then some explosions happen to them!

You sure like explosions, huh?

In a good story, they function as punctuation marks. Hamlet says "To be or not to be", and the building behind him blows up. It is spectacular.
The audience whispers, "Yes. This is what Shakespeare meant."

So your story is Hamlet only with explosions instead of punctuation.

You say it like it's not fan-tastic!

Do the characters even react to the explosions at all?

Sometimes they go off in the background and they barely glance over their shoulder at them. Sometimes they outrun them down halls or by climbing up ladders real fast. It depends on the scene!

THE ULTIMATE STORY FOR MEN:
Hamlet sips some whiskey while punching a man in the nose! Ophelia says she's crazy for him and they go on a helicopter ride. A ghost appears, and when Hamlet high fives him he explodes! Then Denmark explodes.

Later, Ophelia's topless!

people in the stories for men are always showing up to work late, saying "sorry i'm late, mr. bossman! an explosion happened to me." then mr. bossman explodes them out of the office!

1139

when they are old, the two "stories for women" protagonists shake hands and agree that yes, communication was always key in their relationship.

horse barbie is a barbie who has been turned into a horse

when the only tool you have is birth control, all your problems start to look like this thing you can maybe have safe sex with.

i wrote this after reading jeremy tinder's "black ghost apple factory" which i recommend whole-heartedly for the strip "robots don't say i love you"

never so shocked as to forget the who/whom distinction

that "hold the bulb while the world revolves around them" joke doesn't make any sense. that technique would, at best, get one only halfway through the bulb-changing process

AMAZING AND TRUE STORIES FROM THE LIFE OF UTAHRAPTOR

also starring T-REX

This morning I skipped breakfast and met T-Rex for lunch. He seemed excited. He always seems excited.

I asked him why, and it turned out that Dromiceiomimus had a customer service issue with a shipping company, and wanted T-Rex to call because he's better at these sorts of things. They'd failed to deliver her package four times now. T-Rex already has "suckified delivery companies" on his revenge list (he'd said), so he was pleased to call. He spent ten minutes listing all the ways suckified delivery companies had made his life worse, got a full head of steam, and called them up. Long story short, the package had actually been delivered that morning. T-Rex claims victory.

I actually ran into him (almost literally) later that afternoon, and we discussed it some more.

My contrarian position (I freely admit it) was that he was wrong to chew out the lady on the phone: with companies this size, there's no way she was responsible for the package. Responsibility is so diffused that really, nobody is responsible - it's a system failure, and the person in the call centre can't change the system. He replied that as his only contact point, agents should expect complaints and offer solutions - he's not going to make allowances for someone else's broken system. We agreed to differ.

I realize that this is my diary for the new year, and all I've written about so far is T-Rex. The responsibility for this, I feel, lies solely in this Christmas gift "stationary" from T-Rex himself. He's drawn himself in every panel, and the same pre-printed title takes up all the space in the first one. Still, grocery shopping's more fun.

pick up eggs

eggs are great

you can put them on your plate

Microsoft Word WordArt, t-rex? seriously?

in panel 5 utahraptor was supposed to be thinking "i should be more supportive of t-rex's ideas. usually they have nowhere to go but up" but WHOOPS, UTAHRAPTOR OLD BUDDY, NO ROOM FOR THAT! INSTEAD YOU HAVE REACHED A ZEN STATE OF PERFECT THOUGHTLESS AWARENESS

so anyway they were trying to steal the mona lisa (the girl, not the painting)

BUT THEY ARE IN A STORY WHEN THEY TALK ABOUT THIS OH MY GOD

for those of who you don't remember america's funniest home videos, it's basically youtube, but with none of the brutally dumb comments and with way more bob saget. you know, in retrospect, we had it pretty good

be it resolved that monocle guys are the new Other

i spilt it on my bed and it doesn't wash out! hilarious!

T-REX VISITS A GHOST TOWN.

Attention, any ghosts that can hear me! I have one thing to say to you:

this is awesome

LATER:
It was great, Dromiceiomimus: a whole town that had been abandoned! All these collapsing buildings and rusting machines. It was APOCALYPSE PORN.

I'd love to see it!

We should go! It's so great. You get a glimpse of what the world would be like if it all went wrong, and we all died tomorrow!

What actually happened to the town?

The mine dried up and every one moved away!

But the buildings are still there, and they're great. It's cliché, but walking around you see all these amazing little tokens of previous life: a forgotten doll, a can of food long since unidenti-fiable... Dromiceiomimus and I are going back. Want to come?

Sure!

BACK AT THE GHOST TOWN:
It's okay, I guess. It's mostly just a bunch of crappy buildings!

Don't even, Utahraptor!

Don't even what?

Don't even - don't even tell me you don't appreciate the stark aesthetics and beauty of decay

I VALUE OUR FRIENDSHIP BUT SO HELP ME I'LL END IT OVER THIS

what adult life is actually like: "ooh, a new kind of cream cheese! i - i should try this on a bagel."

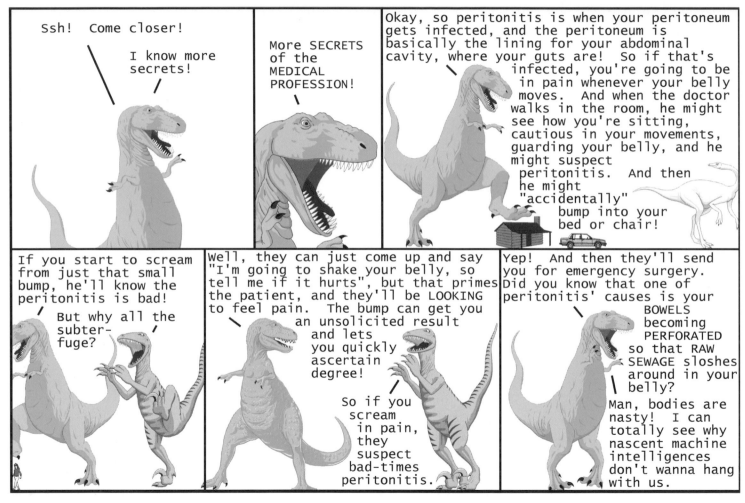

Ssh! Come closer!

I know more secrets!

More SECRETS of the MEDICAL PROFESSION!

Okay, so peritonitis is when your peritoneum gets infected, and the peritoneum is basically the lining for your abdominal cavity, where your guts are! So if that's infected, you're going to be in pain whenever your belly moves. And when the doctor walks in the room, he might see how you're sitting, cautious in your movements, guarding your belly, and he might suspect peritonitis. And then he might "accidentally" bump into your bed or chair!

If you start to scream from just that small bump, he'll know the peritonitis is bad!

But why all the subter-fuge?

Well, they can just come up and say "I'm going to shake your belly, so tell me if it hurts", but that primes the patient, and they'll be LOOKING to feel pain. The bump can get you an unsolicited result and lets you quickly ascertain degree!

So if you scream in pain, they suspect bad-times peritonitis.

Yep! And then they'll send you for emergency surgery. Did you know that one of peritonitis' causes is your BOWELS becoming PERFORATED so that RAW SEWAGE sloshes around in your belly?

Man, bodies are nasty! I can totally see why nascent machine intelligences don't wanna hang with us.

dear diary, why do nascent machine intelligences gotta be such DICKS

guys there's zero hits on google for "customers know what they want, but they want what they know".
i am seriously just WHIPPING OFF quality business advice here!

i wanted more MANLY ADVENTURE NARRATIVE and less WEAK ROMANCE WITH ILSA where the breen censorship code at the time forbade depicting a woman leaving her husband for another man anyway! we already know you will stay with your husband, ilsa! can we cut back rapid-fire quips between the captain and rick now please

oh hey, Uncanny Valley Personified! i see you're making mannequins in your own image. nice! the overly prominent nipples you've added onto both sexes of mannequin body are an indescribably unsettling touch.

even the word "bosoms" is dumb! what is with this friggin' universe anyway.

t-rex, this party is great! it's beyond my ability to reverse engineer!

I AM IN HELL AND THE TORMENTED SOULS HERE JUST SAID "WHAT, DID HE SAY THE N-GAGE? IT ONLY HAS 50 GAMES AND YOU HAD TO REMOVE THE BATTERY PACK TO PUT A NEW GAME IN IT. THAT'S SO WRONG! NOW I FEEL EVEN WORSE ABOUT EVERYTHING!" AND NOW WHAT AM I SUPPOSED TO TELL THEM

YOU CAN STILL USE ALLEGORIES IT'S JUST EVERY TIME YOU DO YOU'LL BE UNDERLINING THE FACT THAT WE'RE NOT LIVING IN THE BEST OF ALL POSSIBLE WORLDS

alternate ending: last panel blank

Synesthesia is an amazing neurological condition in which one sensory pathway involuntarily stimulates another. The result is sensory overlap: tones with distinct tastes, letters of the alphabet with their own shades of colour!

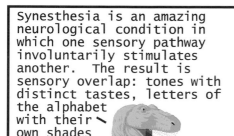

People with synesthesia BASICALLY have super powers.

There's all sorts of synesthesia: some people taste words and syllables when they say them - sometimes even if they just think them! Others have distinct personalities associated with numbers or letters, so that the letter "M" might be polite while "7" gets all up in everyone's fries. They still sense normally, it's just they've got this extra layer of perception on top of what the rest of us get. I admit to being jealous!

I actually know a woman who has synesthesia, T-Rex!

Oh wow! Really?

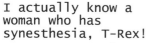

I'd love to meet her. I know she might not be as into her condition as I am and that I'm probably glorifying it or at least fetishizing it some, but I'd still love to talk to her about it!

You are, but it's okay, she's into it too! She loves it, actually. I'll give you her number!

SOON:

So yeah, notes that are higher tend to be brighter colours for me!

I see what you're saying there!

Pretty clever, right? My friends say I'm "pretty clever".

We should date!

TOO STRONG, T-REX

1167

WHY DO WE KEEP HAVING CONVERSATIONS FROM THE FAR SIDES OF THE ROOM

LATER: they all go a'swimmin, and t-rex explains about html

1170

two weeks later: t-rex opens his sales spreadsheet and replaces the 's' in the 'profits' heading with a dollar sign

Okay, so whatever. MAYBE the Terminal Velocity Skateboard Simulator would never reach terminal velocity, since there's no wind resistance. But do we not have an obligation to future generations to make sure??

NOPE

Whatever! If I were in the future and I could open up a book and see "The awesome terminal velocity skateboard didn't work, OH WELL", then I would do that.

I don't think you would, T-Rex! Because you could basically do that today, if you wanted to read up on the physics. The issue is that even with the ground moving, the board is going to slide down the ramp because of gravity.

Ridiculous! There's friction in the wheels that -

- wouldn't be enough!

The treadmill speeds up to match the board's forward momentum, right? But if you've got impossibly perfect bearings, that's just going to make the wheels go faster while the board still slides down. So it's just the friction in the bearings that can keep you in place, and at the levels we're talking about, your wheels would melt first!

FINE. You know what? FINE. I'm done dreaming!

t-rex we symbolically represent sexy babes who forgot our clothes today! wooo!

Okay, NOW I'm done dreaming.

we're still here woooo

we would have our hands raising the roof except that's too hard to draw clearly at this size woooo

1173

Attention, enemies! I am barely resisting an "I'm your biggest fan" joke right now.

a planet full of ahappy people, working boring jobs but not really minding, telling their significant others that love without happiness actually is different from just a really deep satisfaction, repeating it to themselves in the mirror every morning

my friend "P" has a bank card that suggests his middle name is "Spanky." Way to go, P! ALSO, YES, if you are down with P then you are also correspondingly down with me.

joey comeau of a softer world dot com is here, and he says that if they found the nazi pin on me, it would just show people that not ALL nazis are bad. joey comeau: history's greatest monster?

priorities change when you move from a gram to a kilogram.

i spent the entire comic building up ted, the text-to-speech voice guy, and then abandoned him in the last panel for mr. tusks! listen, ted: i have no regrets

originally this comic tied together the car bumper / vacuum robot thing at the end, but then i was like, man, all this just gets in the way of vacuum robot directive three.

I have come up with the ultimate disaster movie! It is called "OH GOSH: A SERIES OF DISASTERS" and what happens is a guy gets out of bed, stubs his toe and says,

"Oh, GOSH!"

Then he falls down the stairs!

Then he smashes through a load-bearing beam at the bottom and his house collapses! And then a spark from a broken lamp ignites the gas, and his house explodes, shooting the guy out into the sky and lighting the surrounding houses on fire. By the time the fire department arrives the entire block is aflame, and also, their fire truck is on fire. Then the fire reaches a power station, causes a cascade failure, and power goes down for the entire country, and soon, the world!

The power failure goes worldwide?

The guys in charge of preventing that were watching the fires on TV!

ANYWAY, things progress and characters keep saying "What is with this... Series of Disasters?" It's so good, Utahraptor. Volcanoes erupt, earthquakes strike, and meteors hit just as soon as all the other stuff gets boring.

And let me guess: at the end the Earth explodes?

Yeah, but after the credits, the original guy wakes up and says "Whew! It was all a dream!" Then he gets out of bed, STUBS HIS TOE, turns to the camera in terror, wide-eyed, and screams "Oh GOSSSSSH!!!"

Holy crap. There's nothing not to like in my movie.

T-Rex's other ultimate disaster movie, "The Earth Stops Spinning and Everybody Flies Into A Wall", can easily be incorporated into the narrative. THE NARRATIVE IS EXPRESSLY DESIGNED TO ALLOW EVERYONE TO FLY INTO A WALL AT POINT OR THREE

1183

cowboy driving his horse hard in front of a chasing lava flow, rearing it up, fully unloading his two revolvers into the molten rock

people whose middle name is "Sheriff": at least I know YOU'RE tough.

COMPRESSED SONG COMICS
"HOLLABACK GIRL"
BY GWEN STEFANI AND
PHARRELL WILLIAMS

Gwen Stefani is not a holla back girl! This is her shit, and it is recognized as bananas.

Bananas is spelt, "b-a-n-a-n-a-s".

THE END

COMPRESSED SONG COMICS
"I CAN'T HELP MYSELF"
BY THE FOUR TOPS

The narrator can't help himself and wants you, and nobody else. You are aware of this. Despite (or because) of this, you, Sugarpie, Honeybunch, left a picture of yourself in his possession, and he kissed it one thousand times.

The narrator denies any personal liability, and says love justifies these actions.

COMPRESSED SONG COMICS
"I WANNA BE LOVED BY YOU"

Marilyn Monroe wants to be loved and kissed by you. She has no greater aspirations and is filled with desire to make you her own.

Boop-boop a-doop.

1186   furthermore, helen kane, betty boop, frank sinatra, rhonda towns, rose murphy, tina louise, and patricia kaas also all want to be loved by you, alone. this is sourced to wikipedia.

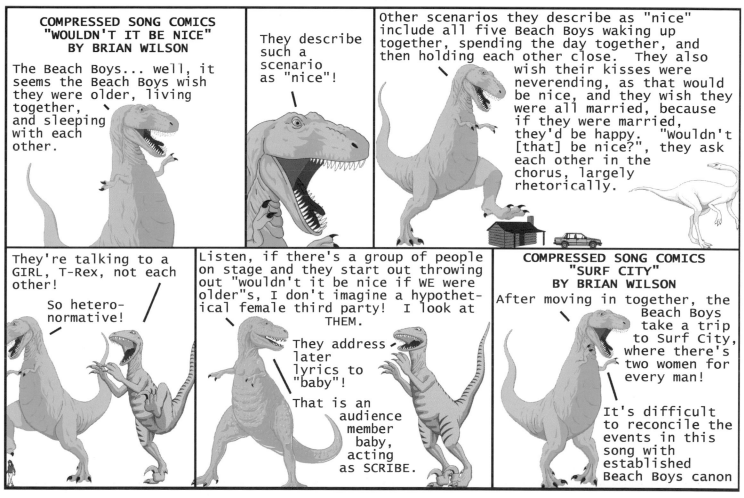

COMPRESSED SONG COMICS "WOULDN'T IT BE NICE" BY BRIAN WILSON

The Beach Boys... well, it seems the Beach Boys wish they were older, living together, and sleeping with each other.

They describe such a scenario as "nice"!

Other scenarios they describe as "nice" include all five Beach Boys waking up together, spending the day together, and then holding each other close. They also wish their kisses were neverending, as that would be nice, and they wish they were all married, because if they were married, they'd be happy. "Wouldn't [that] be nice?", they ask each other in the chorus, largely rhetorically.

They're talking to a GIRL, T-Rex, not each other!

So heteronormative!

Listen, if there's a group of people on stage and they start out throwing out "wouldn't it be nice if WE were older"s, I don't imagine a hypothetical female third party! I look at THEM.

They address later lyrics to "baby"!

That is an audience member baby, acting as SCRIBE.

COMPRESSED SONG COMICS "SURF CITY" BY BRIAN WILSON

After moving in together, the Beach Boys take a trip to Surf City, where there's two women for every man!

It's difficult to reconcile the events in this song with established Beach Boys canon

surf city was actually written by brian wilson with some other non-beach boys, so really, t-rex is concerned about Beach Boys FANON.

1187

SONGS IN LIMERICK FORMAT COMICS

What? What?

THE WHITE STRIPES: SEVEN NATION ARMY

Okay, um: There was a young man who would yell, That we all had a story to tell, Feelings in his bones Said to find a home From the Queen of England to the hounds of hell!

THAT'S REALLY NOT BAD FOR SOMETHING RIGHT OFF THE TOP OF YOUR HEAD

I know, right? Go me!

Is that what we do now? Just shift songs into different formats?

It's fun!

I just was hoping to hear more about you and your life right now, you know? How'd that Nazi Pin thing work out for you?

Okay, honestly, who wants to hear about Nazi pins?

Me! I do.

And INSTEAD, who wants to hear me sing the classic rock power ballad "Total Eclipse of the Heart", while SIMULTANEOUSLY transforming the chorus into one focused on NAUGHTY LIMERICKS??

I do! I do!

Um

You only get one vote, UTAHRAPTOR

you had me at the first mention of emblematic classic rock power ballad 'total eclipse of the heart'

MOM we have had this conversation BEFORE now where did you put my four-fingered white gloves and recordings of raymond scott's "powerhouse" COME ON

1189

A lot of people seem to have trouble separating actors from their roles.

But not me!

I'm different than everyone else. I get that Bruce Willis might not be that useful if terrorists take over an office tower Christmas party!

Come on, T-Rex. You suspect he'd be good to have around. If you were choosing your members for your "taking down terrorists while dying hard" team, you'd pick Bruce first.

Nope. He'd have to earn it! We'd do sports or something to see.

Ridiculous! You confuse actors and the characters they play as much as any of us.

I really don't!

I won't say that I'm "better" for having this skill of "actor separation", but it's a skill I have that makes me better.

You totally like actors if you like their characters, and vice versa. Come on, follow me. I'll prove it.

SOON:

T-Rex, there's Ben Affleck. Do you have anything to say to him?

BEN I QUESTION YOUR ACTING ABILITY! IF WE WERE ALL FRIENDS, I AM CERTAIN YOU WOULD BE "THE IRRITATING ONE"!

Oh my gosh, Utahraptor! I concede your point!

1190

bruce willis: GOOD TO HAVE AROUND?

attention everyone: i agree with panels one through two. splinter did good by those turtle boys.

in researching this comic i kept forgetting what side i was on

1193

A lot of folks get tattoos commemorating life experiences they've had.

Guys! We can do better!

I'm going to get tattoos commemorating life experiences I WISH I'd had. Perhaps a nice banner on my chest that says, "Around The World Race Participant: Giraffe Division!" Or there could be a picture of me, riding a giraffe, and then the giraffe is straddling the world.

I don't think you'd fit on a giraffe, T-Rex.

That's why I'm working in the fanciful medium of the tattoo!

These ideas aren't actually that bad! I think tattoos should be ridiculous.

I know!

I also thought passive-aggressive tattoos would be fun. Like, instead of a heart that says, "Mom", a heart that says "Hey MOM thanks for buying me a private island!" And then when my mom sees it and says "I never bought you that", I can say "Not yet!" and smile!

Moms like that, right?

AT THE TATTOO PARLOUR:
What I want to a to-do list on my hand, only it says "Be awesome" and that's crossed out, and then "Get tattoo" and that's crossed out, and then "Sex up the person reading this".

And you PROMISE you won't regret this?

Sir! I promise nothing!!

if someone wants to create a "tattoos moms like" site, i will be the first to link to it. i am envisioning people with tattoos of themselves cooking a balanced meal, complete with thought bubbles that read "i'm learning how to take care of myself"

t-rex would have said "oh no! are those ALLEGED criminals breaking into my house", but they were already wearing domino masks and carrying a laundry bag with a dollar sign on it

i celebrate Act Like A Logdriver Day, in which i go birling down and down white water. i do believe that's where the logdriver learns to step lightly

if shakespeare was alive today, future historians could just check his blog record and say, "aha! on april 7th his current music was 'linkin park' and his current mood was 'cheezed'. right on."

1200

T-REX IF I SAID NOT TO HAVE SEXY FUN TIMES IN THE PAST IT MUST HAVE BEEN SARCASTIC OR SOMETHING
SO PLEASE FEEL FREE TO HAVE AS SEXY A FUN TIME AS YOU FIND YOU ARE COMFORTABLE WITH

remember when YOU were young and believed no member of the interesting sex could ever find you attractive under their own volition?

A CAUTIONARY TALE!!

"Now they show you how detergents take out bloodstains - a pretty violent image there! I think if you've got a T-shirt with a bloodstain all over it..."

"...maybe laundry isn't your biggest problem!"

Come on, T-Rex. That's plagiarized. That's a Jerry Seinfeld joke.

I know, I know! But he's a funny guy, right? And I was thinking: maybe if I told his jokes, I could get inside his head and understand how he comes up with them. Act like Seinfeld in order to become Seinfeld, you know?

I guess?

This still sounds like an elaborate excuse for plagiarisms!

It's really not meant to be!

INCIDENTALLY, Utahraptor, somebody just gave me a shower radio! Do I really want music in the shower? I guess there's no better place to dance than a slick surface next to a glass door.

Yeah. It was funny when Seinfeld said it a decade ago!

Come on! It's the exact same joke!!

PUBLIC SPEAKING:
Thank you all for listening today. I'm told to always go out on a joke, so here's a classic Seinfeld gag for you: "Newman!"

Wait, no. "Newman."

"NEWMAN."

Yes. There it is!

after discovering the word 'plagiarisms', i'm really not sure why 'plagiarism' should ever be used in the singular anymore. 'timmy! your essay is chock-a-block full... of PLAGIARISMS!!'

if any of my readers explode today due to a loss of atomic cohesion, i'll be all, wow, did i call that or what?

1205

guys! i'm beginning to think that the very concept of Australian Batman is flawed!

i'm literally sick of intensifiers. here, i'll show you. it's just around that tree there.

can you imagine a digestive system running in "full reverse"? it's either entirely horrible, or it's comedy bronze, silver and gold.

Everyone knows I look forward to being an old man - that I covet the societal get out of jail free card that being old gives you! People will say, "Oh, don't mind T-Rex! He always pees on his neighbour's flowers."

"But it's because he's OLD."

But I think my issue is that while I can see myself now (young, vibrant, effervescent) and imagine myself when I'm old (crotchety, petulant, charmingly belligerent), I don't see any in-between stages. The day I start going around with a walker is the day I finally become an old man, and that sucks! That means I'm old as soon as my body's old, and it's way too late to fully enjoy it then.

Don't tell me you're planning to become prematurely old.

It is now my stated intention!!

And I'm going to start it by calling everyone "my boy". How's it going, my boy?

I'm not your boy.

My boy, when you're my age, you get to call all sorts of things all sorts of things!

You're creeping me out. IT DOESN'T WORK IF YOU'RE NOT OLD.

My boy, my boy, my boy.

Myyy boyyyyyyyy

for fun times, try calling people in positions of authority (teachers, police) "my boy". this may depend on your definition of "fun" and to a lesser extent, "times"

1209

Tableau vivant, or "tableau" is a form of theatre in which the actors strike a pose and then don't move! It's like a living picture. It is, in fact, French for "living picture".

And I am the king of tableau, my friends! Check it out:

...TABLEAU!

Um, you're not supposed to speak during tableau, T-Rex!

Beg pardon?

It's motionless AND silent. Interestingly enough, it was favoured by early art photographers, as they already needed their subjects to stay motionless for minutes at a time.

Huh. Interesting.

Anyway. I'm still the best at tableau.

MEANWHILE, IN THE UNIVERSE WHERE T-REX ACTUALLY IS THE BEST AT TABLEAU:

TABLEAU!

I must keep the other actors from discovering my secret to excellent tableau.

It's a very competitive business

victorians had a penchant for naked tableau: nude or topless women weren't allowed on stage, but there was a loophole that allowed them to be seen if they remained perfectly motionless. FACT OR FICTION??

ben emailed me asking when I wrote "dinosaur comics returns monday, with CHUCKLES!" if I meant that i'd be added a new character, called "Chuckles", today. I thought that was awesome, so the director offscreen in panel 6 is officially called "Ben Chuckles". take a bow, mr. chuckles!

1211

i got many emails yesterday with the tip of scaling up the periods and commas. kids today! WHEN WE WERE KIDS, WE JUST MESSED WITH MARGINS AND USED BOOKMAN OLD STYLE, ON ACCOUNT OF HOW IT WAS HECKUVA WIDE

I like it when commercials license pop songs and then make up their own product-centric lyrics. It's a window into an alternate corporate-controlled universe!

An alternate corporate controlled universe where all songwriters have brain damage?

The lyrics are always so terrible and the songs entirely arbitrary. It's like - it's like they license "Candle in the Wind" and then have some Elton John sound-alike singing "Goodbye, Norma Jeane / Did you ever / Use Duracell / They make some fine batteries / On this we all should dwell"

Hah! You know, I'd watch that commercial.

It's so representative!

Now do "Somewhere Over The Rainbow"!

Sure! Um... how about...

"Someone's Sara-Lee branded / cherry pie / makes me glad that I've heard that / they're now in high supply"

Hilarious! It makes me want to buy a Sara-Lee branded cherry pie.

It's not that hard! You just imagine being good, and then don't do that.

THAT EVENING (SET TO THE TUNE OF "WHAT A WONDERFUL WORLD"):

I see leaves of green / red onions too / I see them here, for me and you / And I think to myself: / "What A Wonderful Pre-Packaged Asian-Style Salad from Loblaw's Grocery."

Man, *I* did WAY better than that!!

the radio's turned down. it's not because i couldn't get the lyrics to fit otherwise.

I wrote a story about a man who weeps all the time, but it turns out there actually IS a disease where you cry all the time. Dacryorrhea! I made it up but it already exists.

This is not the first time this has happened!

There's TONS of horrible diseases that sound like they're just made up by somebody, but actually do exist. Fibrodysplasia ossificans progressiva, in which connective tissue becomes bone, freezing a person in place! The Capgras delusion, in which loved ones appear to you to be replaced by identical impostors! And these are just the two I know about.

And THEN, there's the diseases that are familiar because they're so common, but still messed up!

Such as?

Man, Alzheimer's? I mean, I know this disease has always been an issue for me, but it's so terrible. And honestly, it sounds like it's something out of bad fiction. It's ridiculous on the same level as "always cries". It shouldn't happen.

I don't know what to tell you, man!

LATER:
God, how come we live in a world where all these awful diseases exist?

T-REX HOW COME YOU WALK AROUND THE DOWNTOWN CORE NAKED

Man! These two questions better not have the same answer!!

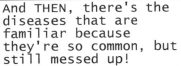

every comic over the past 5 years was just setting the stage for this joke. thanks for reading, everyone!!

DO YOU JUST WANT TO INVITE ME OVER THEN WE CAN PLAY GTA IV AND EAT DELICIOUS SNACKS AND IF YOU SAY NO THEN TELL ME WHAT ABOUT THIS PICTURE I HAVE PAINTED IS POSSIBLY UNDESIRABLE

1219

I have a problem as a reader, as a Consumer of Fictional and Non-Fictional Worlds. My problem is this:

I really don't think dreams are important?

I didn't think that MOST people thought that dreams were all that important, but I must be in the minority, because I keep seeing fiction that uses dreams as Very Significant Symbolism. And the worst is when stories end on these Significant Dreams, because in my mind, I'm thinking "This is ridiculous; when will we get back to the real story? This is entirely irrelevant." and then it's over and I think "Oh. Huh."

You really can't get past your opinion on dreams?

I can't. Nor do I want to!

They're random firings of sleepy brains. They're stupid stuff that my brain does to entertain itself when I'm not around to make it look at chicks or punches.

I mean, I agree with you, but I can still accept dreams as a narrative device.

Never!!

LATER:
Hamlet II dreamed he was the lead singer of C+C Music Factory. He woke up. "C+C Music Factory?" he thought, shaking his head. "How irrelevant." He then focused himself on the seriously erotic business of being Hamlet II.

There! Sex AND politics!

1220

when t-rex says "looking at punches", he means, like, the kind of punches that make people sit down and have birds tweet around their head. not the kind that's in a bowl with a ladle. that one is only sometimes.

When I die, nobody say "He's at peace now", okay? I'm so serious right now.

Say something better, like "I can't believe he ate the whole thing!"

What's wrong with "He's at peace"? It's nice.

It's demeaning! It suggests that the whole point of life is to be at peace, like it's this goal that we should all achieve, and I'M kind of a screw up but at least I achieved it by dying! It's like telling the kids who came in last in a three-legged race that the REAL goal was just to finish.

I think it's supposed to be taken in a "his suffering is over" sort of way.

Oh. Well. That makes more sense.

Did you at least like my comparison of life to a three-legged race?

It was a little confusing! You need a partner for a three legged race, but you can easily go through life profoundly alone.

Wow. That's- that's true.

sigh

LATER:

Hullo T-Rex! Can I ask you a question? It won't take a minute.

Oh, Mr. Tusks! Your delightful minute (as in time) and minute (as in tiny) pun has cheered me right up!!

1222

let's never talk about death again!

all except dr. sensible are newly-graduated medical students known to me.

The problem with Superman, and Spider-Man, AND Batman, and pretty much every other superhero, is that their stories don't have ends. They're all stuck in the same productive age range, 20-30 years old, and it's easy to see why!

Companies don't want their most popular characters dying of old age!

But the result is that their stories don't have ENDS. We don't know how Batman deals with a failing body and the rigours of old age, how Spider-Man reacts when Mary Jane loses her looks. I mean, we DO, because sometimes out-of-continuity stories explore this, but they're never for real - they don't count! Bats is always 30 again in the next issue. It's like David fights Goliath, but they keep fighting every few issues for 50 years, and you never see how it ends.

You know, there are a lot of interesting parallels here with soap operas!

How so?

Soaps have long-running narratives, but characters die all the time. The difference is soaps focus on premise rather than individuals, so they're not killing a cash cow when someone dies. They just bring in someone new!

So Batman dies, and the book focuses on his butler Alfred working for Spider-man instead!

Sir, I am old and conservative. You can't expect me to "loosen up" overnight.

Alfred, I'm young and liberal! I don't like your "rules"!!

Gentlemen, gentlemen!! Please!

YES.

well, it seems your mortgage application forms are all in order! i like that in a woman.

"HORSES VS. TRAINS"

Ah, the age-old debate! Horses are okay.

If you don't have any trains around, that is!!

Horses eat grass. Trains are huge multi-ton machines that GET THINGS DONE. And then when you think trains are as great as it gets, you discover maglev trains! These are literal HOVERTRAINS that wrote in their diaries, "Screw it, diary! I'm just gonna go as fast as I can from now on!!" and then they go 581 km/h like it's no big deal. NICE.

Horses eat grass, and SOMETIMES, hop over buckets.

I guess the old stereotype of boys liking trains is true!

Come on, that's dumb!

I like trains because they're big complicated machines that NOT ONLY get folks places quickly, but also, threaten maidens tied to the tracks by mustachio-twirling villains. If horses could do that I would like horses too.

I'm pretty sure horses CAN do that.

WELL THEN. I GUESS I'M A FAN OF HORSES.

LATER:

EXCUSE ME LIBRARIAN DO YOU HAVE ANY BOOKS ON HORSES

Yes sir! We have many books on many topics, here at your local library!

THANK YOU

PRETTY SURE ONE WILL SUFFICE

what you have to picture is a horse raising a hoof like a fist and menacing it at the maiden. if you were already picturing that before you started reading this comic, hey, you're way ahead of the game

1227

1228

this is called "a grim portrait of a world without backspace"

WIKIPEDIA! I would have donated during your last funding drive, if only I knew!!

this happened to me once, only i kept wiping my nose in my sleep, so it was my hands that were covered in blood when i woke up. i saw my hands, and was like, "dear diary, all i remember is watching half a movie and falling asleep on the couch?"

WHAT IS YOUR FAVOURITE CARTOON STEREOTYPE COMICS

Oh man. The heart-pounding out-of-the-chest "I'm in love" reaction shot!

Second ONLY to the "I'm so angry my head is now a steamwhistle, toot toot" motif!

If I had three wishes - and the wishes had to be about cartoon stereotypes being real, I guess - then those are the two I'd choose. The third one would be "no falling when running off cliffs unless you look down and notice you're running on air", because that, my friends, would be HANDY.

Free bridges for the strong-willed!

I would have thought you'd choose the bullet hole / water one!

Which one's that?

It's the one where you're shot with a machine gun, and then later you're thirsty, and then you drink water, and then the water springs out of the holes in your body.

Hilarious!! Plus, it offers some resistance to machine gun fire.

Exactly! It's right up your alley.

T-REX IN HEAVEN THE BULLET HOLE WATER THING HAPPENS TO ANYONE WHO DIED FROM BEING MACHINE GUNNED IN THE CHEST

LISTEN

I HAVE BEEN WORKING ON A SOLUTION

IN THE MEANTIME EVERYONE JUST SIMMER DOWN AND EAT JELLO INSTEAD OF WATER
HALF OF YOU WERE WISHING FOR THIS WHEN YOU WERE SIX ANYWAY

"it presupposes you equate every part of yourself with the whole! WHAT'S THE DEAL"

1233

pedophile jokes, here at qwantz.com! also: HELLO GOVERNMENT WATCHDOGS, THANK YOU FOR YOUR KEYWORD LOOKUPS. I HOPE YOU ENJOY MY COMIC TODAY

1235

You know those suicide barriers that are placed on some bridges? They're usually things like closely-spaced metal wires going up and running the length of the bridge, to prevent folks from hopping over the edge.

They freak me right the heck out!

They're such a crazy symbol for our society! We have them there because if we didn't, MEMBERS OF OUR COMMUNITY would kill themselves. We need physical barriers to stop this from happening. If you look at it as a benchmark for our society, it's so weird! We have to change our environment to make it difficult to off ourselves, otherwise we'd all be committing suicide? What are we doing wrong?

Come on, society doesn't make us all suicidal! It only makes a FEW people suicidal.

Sure!

But even so, if suicidal folks really want to kill themselves, these barriers won't stop them. They'll just go somewhere else.

But they DO prevent spur of the moment suicides!

These are symptoms! We should be working on causes!

Social programs do work on the causes!!

SUICIDE IN COMICS

"WHAT IS THE DEAL"

1236

oh look, an ALIVE person has an opinion on suicide!

I've been writing a romance novel!

Or more precisely, I've been sucking SURPRISINGLY HARD at writing a romance novel!

It's terrible, Dromiceiomimus! All my life I was certain that explosions could spice up ANY narrative, but I've been blowing my main characters up ALL THE TIME and they're still not that interesting! Check this out: "Antonio Tony and Samantha were explosive-expert friends who decided one day to try kissing each other. It wasn't that bad! Later on, one of them decided that it was actually pretty bad."

THE END?

I think your problem is you're focusing on plot!

How do you figure?

Romance is about two CHARACTERS meeting and falling in love, but all you've got is narrative. We don't really know anything about your protagonists, so we don't care what happens to them. Flesh them out!

Oh kay!

Samantha was a cowgirl, always on the lookout for a SPUR-of-the-moment marriage Antonio Tony was a horse enthusiast. "I hope to be SADDLED with a wife soon!" he thought to himself. They waved wildly at each other across the open plains.

Utahraptor, come quick! My story's amazing!!

"It beHOOVES us to get married soon," said Antonio Tony. "Oh, Tonio," said Samantha, sighing. "I don't like horse puns THAT much."

if you don't read the times new roman text as t-rex composing in his head, you end up with a post-modern comic in which author and character collaborate on composing erotica. DO NOT READ IT THIS WAY, OKAY??

there are a lot of logistical problems with zombie ghosts that i concede i am unable to quickly resolve

it is a word that is very handy if you are in the alien movies and a friend of yours has an alien pop out of his chest. you won't struggle for words in that situation anymore.

my friend with the arrow in his eye and i ran around and high tenned each other while shouting 'sawesome!!'? later, i helped him get to the hospital.

Panel 1: Guess who had their first nightmare EVER last night? If you guessed me, then HELLS YES that was the correct guess!

Panel 2: T-REX'S FIRST NIGHTMARE

Panel 3: A bunch of us were hanging out in a house, some went outside, and then a nuclear bomb was dropped in the distance and we could see a mushroom cloud in the sky. I ran to the door to close it and pressed up against it as the windows in the house blew inward and radioactive dust covered us all. THEN, after it was quiet and we ventured outside, I ran into my friends who survived, but we all agreed we'd had too much radiation and wouldn't make it. It was really realistic!

Panel 4: Sounds like a pretty standard nightmare, my friend!

I know! I was stoked!

Panel 5: But then these - stupid atomic zombies showed up? And they started zapping us with cheap-ass lightning bolts coming out of their eyes? It was super dumb, Utahraptor. It was that cheap 60s lightning where they just draw it directly on the film.

Zombies don't even have lightning powers!

Panel 6: The REAL nightmare was how poorly my subconscious understands zombies!

Also the atomic bomb being dropped on you.

That as well.

Someone thinks my email address belongs to somebody else! They keep sending me pictures of their newborn baby, addressed to one "René Wellek". As such, I HAVE BECOME RENÉ WELLEK.

The course of my life has now been set!

Normally when this happens, I write back the sender and let them know they've got the wrong address, but this time is different. They sent me four separate sets of baby pictures, covering the first four days of her life! I've already seen this baby grow up four days! I have a RELATIONSHIP with her now, and I've decided: I'm in for the long haul.

You're not going to correct them?

Nope!

I've become their silent friend René, watching this baby grow up over the years. I'll see her first steps! Her first birthday! And in 18 or so years, I'll have tears in my eyes as my computer pings and her high school grad pictures download into my inbox...

Little creepy, T-Rex!

THAT EVENING:
Okay, here's the news: I am not your friend René but I am just as good. My name is T-Rex and I am a good role model. I brush my teeth regularly and when I forget to I tell myself to try HARDER. Basically, what I am saying here is "I am a stranger on the internet who has taken a particular interest in your child

Perfect!

apparently, rene's email is something easily confused with or very close to 'didyouseeterminatortwo@guysistillreallylikethatmovie.com'

the alternate ending: T-Rex says "God? Is it possible for you to use grammar SO POORLY that even you can't understand what you were trying to say?" and God says "UM HELLO" and then he says "YOU'RE THE DUDE WITH THE BAD APOSTROPHES"

COMPRESSED FILM COMICS
today's film:

WARGAMES

I am Matthew Broderick: computer hacker!

And I've accidentally wardialed my way into a secret military computer that I mistake for a game developer's machine. I believe I will play this mysterious game called "GLOBAL THERMONUCLEAR WAR".

Let's bomb Los Angeles!

Kay! Incidentally, I use an acoustic coupler as a modem, and that's so retro it's cool again.

No argument here

I'm a US Military Agent!

Holy smokes!

You're under arrest for hacking into our computer and also it's still playing your game and it controls our nukes and it's definitely going to start WW]|[by launching them against the Soviets. Cold War, remember?

No worries! I will teach it the MADness of its actions through zillions of tied games of Tic-Tac-Toe!

LATER:

A strange game, Matthew Broderick. It seems the only winning move is not to play.

Oh my God, I love this movie.

Man, me too! They should totally do a crossover with me and Skynet.

ERROR 22: IDEA IS TOO AWESOME

1246

OMNI CONSUMER PRODUCTS BUYS OUT THE US MILITARY AND OBTAINS WOPR AND MAKES IT FIGHT SKYNET. I HAVE CALCULATED THIS TO BE AN AMAZING TALE. LISTEN. COMPUTERS DO NOT MAKE MISTAKES, OKAY?

Panel 1: In fascism, one person is in control of an entire country, and he tells everyone else what to do! He is the guy who is micromanaging his zergs or whatever.

Panel 2: Maybe this is not so bad?

Panel 3: It is so bad, T-Rex! Fascism is bad news!! I mean, YES it is, but what if the one guy KNEW what everyone should be doing? What if he was actually the best person to be in charge of the country? Some people would still want to be free! But WHAT IF he recognized that and let those people be free?

Panel 4: You're saying if there was a guy who could produce a utopia, you'd want him in charge. Exactly! Yes!

Panel 5: Okay, but that's not fascism. Fascism is authoritarian and includes these ideas of unity and purity and stuff like that. It's a sort of a xenophobic, culty nationalism? Oh! I don't like THOSE parts. Well, I guess I don't want to to be fascist after all!

Panel 6: SWEET PROTEST SIGNS L@@K, SO @WESOME!!!OMG YOU GUYS >:OGC

Okay you are bidding on some protest signs that I'm selling because I was gonna be fascist, but not anymore!! There's a picture of me and beneath it they say "T-REX IS IN CHARGE NOW; I GUESS WE'LL ALL JUST HAVE TO DEAL". They have many uses such as pretending that I am in charge and that you are all "no WAY is that guy in charge, what will i do, oh wait my sign says i should just deal"

STARTING BID: $100
YOUR BID: $0

1248

OGC guy! He's back, and he's KINDA CHEESED.

a LITTLE respect, please!

Recently I have discovered something that disturbs me! My savings account is now less negligible than before, and yet - I kinda want some money?

This is not the person I thought I was!

When I was a kid I always thought that as long as I had enough money to live without fear of poverty, I'd be fine. I just wanted enough to get by. But now - I'm treating money like Life Points™, Dromiceiomimus! And I want more Life Points™. I want the high score, and I want the scoreboard to say "TRX" at the top, right above "USA" and "ASS".

I think this is just a matter of figuring out a different sort of Life Points™!

I agree! We've got to find something else for you before you've become a cruel amalgam of the uncles Scrooge and Pennybags!

But what?

How about instead of counting money, you count the number of lives you've touched in a positive way?

Oh God. Listen, I want something more like "Number of Enemies That Said 'I Wish I Wasn't T-Rex's Enemy Anymore', Frig". In fact, that's perfect.

You realize that now you're living for revenge?

Oh! People say that's bad, right? Do you, um, remember any reasons why, off the top of your head?

Well -

Look, are any sayings about how it's WORSE than living for money?

utahraptor, people living for revenge get to walk slow-motion in front of more explosions than heartless plutocrats do. i can't just ignore that

1251

1252

Maybe I have been too hard on prenups. In a sense, they're sort of a Love Validator, right?

PRENUPTIAL AGREEMENTS:

WELL, MAYBE THIS IS THE DEAL

Because if you have a prenup that says, "WOW, NOBODY'S getting rich off this marriage", then it's clear that nobody's getting married for the money. The only reason left is love!

Or loneliness.

Or love! The prenup is a way of announcing AND VERIFYING that you love them for Who They Are, not for what they've got in their pants! In their wallet in their pants!

It was a great metaphor, Dromiceiomimus.

You know, Judaism has long had the "ketubah", which is basically a prenup!

Really!

Yep! It specifies divorce penalties but also marital vows, and is hung up in the house. Prenups can mean a lot of different things to people!

Huh! Maybe the best way to learn about prenups is to get one. Oh my gosh, Utahraptor!! Let's get a "friend-ship prenup"!

Hah! What?

LATER, T-REX HAS COMPLETED HIS PRENUP! WHAT'S IT SAY, T-REX?

It says "Utahraptor! Don't steal my comics, UTAHRAPTOR." Then there's a drawing of him stealing my comics with an x through it!

A LAWYER drew it for me.

1254

Readers! I'm lying! It's not dinosaurs that can't go 2 days without water. IT'S HUMANS!! IT WAS HUMANS ALL ALONG

the court rules that the plaintiff must discern the difference between "natural law" and "positive law", and must ALSO stop imploring the jury to "set right what once went wrong"

T-REX HAS WRITTEN A STORY ABOUT A DOG THAT GETS SUPER POWERS!

It's awesome! It was about a dog who didn't have super powers, and then one day, he got some super powers.

BUT THERE IS A DOWNSIDE:

Now everyone thinks MY dog has super powers!

I don't know at what point we all decided that authors aren't allowed to just make things up anymore, but it's totally what's happened to me! Somehow our fictions have all become real, and "write what you know" is the only creative option.

People actually think your dog has super powers?

Well, they think he's so great he INSPIRED the super powers. He's actually just - really angry?

But that's the thing! Even if I write about something implausible, folks assume there's a real-life inspiration! Come on, T-Rex!

A lot of your previous stories WERE autobiographical. "My Tiring Day"? "A Story About Me (At The End I Sit Down and Write The Book You're Now Reading)"? If I were you, I'd write my next book such that if people DID assume it was about me, it would be flattering.

Yes! Like "The day I Was EXTRA Nice To The Homeless"!

LATER, T-REX PUBLISHES HIS NEW BOOK! IT'S CALLED "LOLITA 2: THE PREQUEL! NOW LOLITA'S EVEN YOUNGER"

Aw craps.

why oh why did i make lolita EVEN YOUNGER

1257

Today is a good day I think for fixing my life! I'll do it by putting out a new, less controversial book: "LOLITA III: This Time, She's 30".

Nobody can argue with that!!

In my story there's a new Lolita, and she's thirty, and she goes out with a man who's also thirty and from a similar economic and social background! They get married and have some okay times. Years later, all the characters die of old age!

It seems a bit - conservative!

I could make some changes! But did you notice how everyone was clearly of the age of majority though?

THE BOOK IS PUBLISHED:

T-Rex, your new book is basically terrible!

gasp

I'm serious! The "new Lolita" has nothing to do with the old one, and nothing interesting happens except when "LoHEta" shows up, explains that he's the new manly male Lolita, and then leaves the narrative entirely.

He shows up again in the epilogue! Utah-raptor! You didn't even finish my book!!

At the end, Loheta addresses the reader directly and explains that if you replace "she" with "he" and "hers" with "definitely his" in the ORIGINAL Lolita, you can read all about his adventures!

It's called "setting up a spinoff"; look it up?

the brilliant thing about loheta is that if anyone gets mad at his book's content, they have only themselves to blame, as they constructed the story they're reading! reputation: salvaged.

guys who has stubbed his little toe so hard that he's broken it, multiple times? OH LOOK IT'S ME, GOOD OLD HARD-WALKIN' RYAN

1259

Hey, it's Utahraptor! Wait - IS that Utahraptor...? Oh my God! It's... IT'S....

Dromiceiomimus, you won't believe who I just met!

Who?

FUTURE UTAHRAPTOR! I'm serious, I saw him! He looked like Utahraptor, but he was aged thirty years, and it was the Most Amazing Thing. It couldn't have been anyone else! It was CLEARLY thirty years older Utahraptor.

So what happened then?

Well, I was staring!

And you noticed it, obviously, but then you turned to me, made eye contact, and nodded with an almost undetectable Mona Lisa smile, just once. It was this amazing nod that said, "Don't worry, T-Rex. Things will be alright. Everything's gonna work out fine."

Hah! Future me's awesome.

MEANWHILE, FORTY YEARS IN THE FUTURE!

Dear audio diary!

i miss my friend utahraptor

1260

i hope he comes home soon. from his month-long vacation in the tropics, that is!

it's always best to talk back to big media like they're lassie. what's that, television? you say traffic volume is high in the downtown core? we've got to do something!!

more accurately, t-rex would have easily won if he'd made the argument before the invention of written language. but then the punchline doesn't work! you can't just build the hms sinkytowne out of words!!

how do we know when and how words changed pronunciation, if they weren't written down? well sir, we look at sucky rhymes in poems and presume they used to work, and also at books written during the shift complaining how kids today keep talkin' wrong

i read one theory for the cause of the great vowel shift that said there may have been a lot of influential people in england with speech impediments, and we all copied them. attention linguists! more theories like this one plz

1266

ONE DAY SCIENCE IS GOING TO FIGURE OUT ULTIMATE SURPRISE AND THE SCIENTIST WHO DOES IT IS GOING TO GO TO HEAVEN HIGH FIVING EVERYONE ON THE WAY UP

Computers have gotten way better in recent years. A new computer can beat a moldy old one from twenty years ago!

FACT.

Wouldn't it be great if rhetoric had evolved in the same way? I could have this hyper-evolved speaking that could convince anyone to do whatever I say, as long as they didn't have similar rhetorical powers to match! Anyone not inured to my amazing powers of speechifying would be putty in my hands. "Oh, T-Rex, I'm not sure I should do this" they'd say, and then I'd say "Oh maybe you should though" and they'd be all, "Awesome."

It would be a disaster for society!

Rude, my friend!

I meant if there was such an advance. Early language learners acquire languages the best, so it would be a generation of toddlers convincing their parents that letting them poop their pants is sweet. If you don't see what's bad for society in that, well - enjoy pooping your pants!

The word 'poop' is cool: it's transitive, but only for 'pants'. You can pee your pants too though. Maybe it's the noun 'pants'? Further research certainly seems warranted.

Maybe I will, Utahraptor! MAYBE I'LL ENJOY POOPING MY PANTS EACH AND EVERY DAY!!

EACH AND EVERY DAY! EVERY MORNING AFTER BREAKFAST! WAIT, THAT'S GROSS. NEVERMIND. LISTEN, CAN YOU THINK OF ANY OTHER VERBS THAT CAN APPLY TO "PANTS" TRANSITIVELY?

1270

1272

his parents come home and say "oh god who made a truck out of human flesh and put it in our son's room. oh god, it's warm, oh god, oh god" and then they throw up. and that's only the first two panels!!

'conspiracies!!' is said in much the same way as one might say 'ice cream!!' on a warm summer's day

space restrictions in panel six forced me to cut five paragraphs of stunt description. basically it was the stunt
driver pulling every stunt ever pulled, back to back, WHILE SHE PUNCHED OUT TERRORISTS WHO DESERVED IT

1276

this problem could be avoided if sexy images of men and women in swimsuits, wearing mortarboards and pointing to a blackboard on which the subject of the article was written, were inserted mid-way through each article. DON'T KNOCK IT UNTIL YOU'VE TRIED IT

COMICS IN WHICH T-REX HAS DEVELOPED SUPER HEALING POWERS, WHICH ALLOW HIM TO RECOVER FROM ANY INJURY ALMOST INSTANTLY

I wonder if today is a lovely day to go on a walk!

Hey! It IS a lovely day to go on a walk!

ANYWAY T-REX NEVER INJURED HIMSELF THAT DAY AND THE POWERS WORE OFF SOON AFTER

THE END

T-REX'S GREATEST FEAR COMICS

My greatest fear is having superpowers and not realizing it!

Really?

Oh my God, I'm TERRIFIED of missing out. I might have elevated strength, but I never try to lift a skyscraper over my head, you know? How would I discover which muscles to flex to make lasers shoot out of my hands?

Hah!

I'm serious! It is The Worst Life.

I don't know I have powers, and over and over again I stand by as everyone close to me gets injured OR WORSE in accidents I could have easily prevented, if only I knew!

Utahraptor! When I die I get an award for "Most Opportunities Missed" and nobody claps!!

1278 a man witnesses all these horrible accidents throughout his life, friends and acquaintances dropping like flies, killed in all these horrible ways. when he finally dies of old age he finds himself in the award ceremony, and he's told about the powers he had, and and he wins the award. everyone in the audience is bandaged. XERIC GRANT PLZ

Shakespeare, I'd just - I'd love to have some precedent to point to for a burn made down the road.

a guy who acts like a big weiner, or a guy who literally is a giant weiner? whichever is more hilarious; it is probably the latter

DIFFERENT WAYS TO MEET NEW PEOPLE TO DATE

a comic for dudes and ladies who are newly single and who are like, man, SCREW THIS

METHOD 1: TAKE UP SPORTS!
You can meet people at sports!

I GUESS

METHOD 2: ASK YOUR FRIENDS IF THEY HAVE ANY SEXY FRIENDS THEY COULD INTRODUCE YOU TO!

Beyond me, that is!

YES. YOU SHOULD DEFINITELY SAY "DO YOU HAVE ANY SEXY FRIENDS, BEYOND ME, THAT IS" AND THEN DATE WHOEVER THEY COME UP WITH

METHOD 3: DATE YOUR BEST FRIEND'S SIBLING!
Don't date my siblings, T-Rex!

FINE

METHOD 4: GOING UP TO STRANGERS AND SAYING "EXCUSE ME, BUT YOU ARE INCREDIBLY ATTRACTIVE!"
That's kinda sketch. It can go either way but I think it veers wildly towards Sketchtowne.

WHAT IF YOU THRUST YOUR HIPS AFTERWARDS

That - doesn't help?

METHOD 5: RANDOM SELECTION FROM THE PHONE BOOK!
Excuse me, are you "Jennifer Klug"?

Yes? Are you on speakerphone?

Jennifer - yes. Do you want a boyfriend who's only a little desperate?

jennifer. jennifer, what if i told you that your name was the most intriguing on all of page 210?

remember the time traveller spammer who needed a dimensional warp generator, back in 2003? i - well, i hope he got his dimensional warp generator

1283

oh my god, that's horrible. in happier news, i did manage to avoid the dog when this happened to ME yesterday morning, and have scratched up my right side. wear a helmet everyone! otherwise today's comic would have been "THANX FOR READING I'M DEAD NOW, BUT GUYS, IT WAS A REALLY CUTE DOG"

Tired of every day being the same of the last?

Maybe?

Maybe just a little?

Then MAYBE you should try my great idea of assigning an emotion to every day of the calendar!!

For example, January 1st could be "excited". And then January 2nd could be "elated". And then January 3rd could be "disgust".

So we all have to be excited on January 1st?

No, but it's like - we're aware of it! So it COLOURS the day, and gives us something to look forward to. Every day becomes a holiday! "March 3rd is contentment day!", we'll say. "I hope it comes soon."

I find it hard to believe you've come up with 355 (to 356) different emotions!

I basically have!

I could only come up with about 20 emotions, but I doubled that by adding "very". Then I doubled them again by adding "not very" and "inappropriately". There's - there's more adverbs.

I'm not sure if it'll -

I'm doing it and it's gonna be great!!

BUT IT IS BAD NEWS FOR FIRST DATES:

Today's Awkward Day, eh? God knows I've already got enough of that!

Hah hah hah

sigh

you might be thinking, "where's t-rex's date in panel 6?" panel 6 comes after t-rex has announced he has to go to the bathroom, and he's stopped and turned to say this to his date for some reason. the whole restaurant can hear. IT'S SO AWKWARD

1285

I CAUTION YOU / IN DEFEATING ORCS WE MAY FIND THE ONLY VILLAIN LEFT TO FACE IS OUR OWN PREJUDICE

years from now folks will have forgotten ever saying "you just got schooled" and the pun in my last panel will seem really forced and weird. THIS I PREDICT

1287

it's been puzzling me of late

1290

"positive change takes TIME, past me. check it out: i didn't even mean for that to be a pun, just good advice!"

1291

"Tina's Curse"
by Utahraptor.

Tina Rex was a woman with a curse. Tina Rex was a woman with a very peculiar curse.

Ever since she was six, Tina Rex knew that she was one day to wake up as a man!

She had been given this curse by her stepmother, who hated her, and presumably men as well. The curse didn't scare Tina. Failing to meet monthly progress reports scared her, missing a checkpoint on her Five-Year Plan scared her, but being a man was like being a woman, she figured, only with more prostate exams. She smiled at her joke. Tina Rex woke up as a man on her 31st birthday.

So! Did you read my rewrite of your comic?

IT WAS SO TERRIBLE

Okay, listen, you're not allowed to rewrite my stories anymore. Prostate exam jokes? Seriously? I stopped reading it three panels in.

What? It got better! It got great!

It sure did, once I rewrote it extensively!!

TINA, *THE DUDE WHO PUNCHED THE FUTURE*

Tina is a woman who can Punch The Future. This means that she'd punch somewhere, and then three weeks later you'd walk over there and go "Ow who punched me." One time she punched a monocle guy who said "Ow, my crotch!" and then he turned around and he said "Ow, my bum!"

THE END?

alternate endings: "Nothing, YOUR HONOUR", "Nothing, PROFESSOR", "Nothing, SECRET SERVICE AGENT HIDING IN MY ROOM AND TRYING TO SPY ON ME AND DOING A TERRIBLE JOB OF IT. THAT'S RIGHT. YOU'RE NOT SUPPOSED TO TALK."

1293

1294   is a man not entitled to leaving his socks in the kitchen? "no", says the man in the basement suite, "we share that space". "no", says the man in the room down the hall, "that's gross and nasty". you... rejected those answers.

Guys, I'm sorry to be the bearer of bad news, but, well, here we are. I should just say it.

Bingo is totally suboptimal and inefficient!

Check it out: replace the caller with a computer, and you make the bingo numbers get called like a billion times faster. Replace the bingo players with other computers, and you speed up the rate at which the game is played. Tie both these innovations together and you can play HUNDREDS of bingo games per second! ONCE AGAIN, something has been made orders of magnitude more efficient by simply replacing all life involved with cold and soulless bingo-playing machines.

But the fun of thing is in dabbing the numbers, in building up suspense as the game progresses. You've made it boring!

Nope!

My new, hyper-efficient bingo is basically like putting in your money, pressing a button, and being informed whether or not you've won.

Exactly!

But that's what slot machines do, and people LINE UP to play them! OH SNAP! IS THIS ANOTHER ARGUMENT WON BY T-REX??

THREE DAYS LATER:

HEY UTAHRAPTOR! DO YOU REMEMBER THREE DAYS AGO, WHEN I TOTALLY BEAT YOU IN AN ARGUMENT?

TO BE HONEST

I'M KINDA LINGERING ON IT

I HAVE BEEN TALKING LIKE THIS FOR DAYS

It turns out there are some regions where my HyperBingo™ is played. Neat!

And it's all thanks to legal loopholes!

AS IT HAPPENS, in some areas gambling is heavily regulated, but bingo is a special case that isn't. And so companies have built electronic bingo machines, exactly as I envisioned! What's more, some have used bingo as an engine to power other types of gambling, like poker and slot machines. The game plays a hidden bingo game, and if you get a bingo, your slots will ALWAYS come up as three cherries. It's nuts! Bingo's being used in ways GOD NEVER INTENDED.

But how do they translate bingo into poker? You have choice over what cards stay in your hand!
They CHEAT!

Say you got a quick bingo, and that translates to a royal flush. You're doomed to win! If you throw away all your cards, you're just gonna get dealt the same flush in a new suit. Even if you try to lose, the computer will step in and CHANGE YOUR CARDS, or just make you win the next game.
Insane!

MEANWHILE, IN THE FUTURE!
CITIZENS! YOU HAVE ABUSED THE POWER OF BINGO, AND WE BINGO-POWERED CYBORGS ARE THE PRODUCT OF YOUR BINGO-POWERED HUBRIS. GUESS IF WE ARE GOING TO DESTROY ALL ORGANIC LIFE!
Y- yes?
ONE WORD:
BINGO.

It's not even a game where your role can easily be replaced by a machine. It's a game where you could easily be replaced AND if you don't play optimally, the machine will step in and kick you out. If ever there was a system designed to make the computers running it become thoroughly exasperated with organic life, THIS IS IT.

1297

1298 friends, i dream of an age of creatures who could high five with their hands and their butts at the same time. i dream of a world where the burden of proof is on the skeptic if a given theory is sweet enough

frig, my spanish stereotypes are just as out of date as my ideas of what day it is!!

everyone who emailed me yesterday saying "thanks, i thought it was monday but your comic reminded me it was tuesday!", now i must tell you: comics are sometimes FULL OF LIES

A button has popped off of one of my favourite shirts!
Will NO-ONE sew it back on for me?
Dromiceiomimus, YOU'RE a good friend! Would you sew a button back onto one of my shirts?
I could, but this is something you should really learn to do for yourself, T-Rex!
But that's the thing: everyone else has ALREADY learned how to do it, so I'd be needlessly duplicating their efforts if I learned it myself!
You're justifying laziness through minimizing inefficiencies?
Exactly! At the societal level!
If only 25% of the population learnt button sewing AND everyone had four friends, then we'd expect one friend to do the button sewing when needed, and the remaining three could use that free time to learn something else! SOCIETY ADVANCES.
I'm not sewing your button on either, T-Rex.
YEARS LATER:
Excuse me, sir: this is a black tie dinner, and you've shown up completely naked.
I blame society!!
Sir
That is not yet on my list of acceptable excuses

a button has popped off one of my favourite shirts! in addition, all of the buttons have also popped off all of my shirts. and pants. and i think i learned to dress wrong.

joey comeau of a softer world dot com sometimes doesn't do title text on his comics. joey comeau of a softer world dot com needs to smarten up fast.

1303

what if someone did it for comics OH GOD

The issue in an ongoing series is once you've done it and it wasn't a fluke, it's like you've shown that one of your characters got Superman powers. And then in the next episode when a building is about to fall over on someone, Superman's running around in circles saying "Oh no what do we do? Frig frig frig" and the audience is sitting there, furrowing their brows, one hand on their chin.

Panel 1:
You know those guys who have been hiccuping for 70 years or whatever? I'm glad I'm not one of those guys.

Panel 2:
Hiccuping forever is this weird sort of... forced immortality!

Panel 3:
But I thought you were all about going down in history, T-Rex?

It's true! But on my own terms. I can't control hiccups, so it's really being remembered for something that my body's doing that's really incidental to who I am, you know? Anyone who heard of me would know me as The Hiccup Guy, and it would overshadow anything else I did with my life.

Panel 4:
I think if you cured cancer or something, we'd still know your name!

True!

Panel 5:
But the headlines would still be "Hiccuping Doctor Cures Cancer". It's too memorable to overlook! I like the choosing my OWN destiny.

Okay, so go to that. Choose your own adventure.

Utahraptor, that reference has instantly inspired me to be the best I can possibly be!!

Panel 6:
LATER, T-REX DISCOVERS THAT 80S REFERENCES WORKED INTO CONVERSATION INSPIRE HIM MORE THAN ANYTHING!

We're focusing too much on the mistakes of the past. Let's get back to the future, shall we?

YES!! YES, LET'S DO THAT!

HOLY CRAP!

1308

he's at a board meeting. it's the future! maybe he snuck in?

so... why don't you and i go back to your place, put on some nice romantic music, swear each other to silence, and make up a great story we can tell our friends?

If we don't celebrate these holidays, who will?

what you can't see in the last panel are t-rex's thoughts, which are transcribed (verbatim) as "aw man! the one time i didn't pick 'boner'."

guys the more you look at it the more the phrase "box office" is kinda ridiculous

So, SOMETIMES, archeologists find things that don't belong in their geological contexts: shells where there were no oceans, that sort of thing. And there's lots of explanations like "maybe an animal ate it and pooped it out, GROSS."

But sometimes these objects are found with human remains!

And when that happens they call it a manuport: something that was carried by hand by ancient dead dudes. Manuports are neat because they show you what ancient dead dudes found interesting! And the most awesome manuport is the oldest one, called the Makapansgat pebble. It dates to 3 million years ago!

There weren't humans around to carry it 3 million years ago, T-Rex!

Nope!

But there were PROTOHUMANS. Austra-lopithecines! And the Makapansgat pebble has this natural "eye eye mouth" face shape on it. A protohuman had enough curiosity and aesthetic sense, 3 MILLION YEARS AGO, to see the face in the rock, and thought it was special enough to carry around with him until he died.

I think it's beautiful and amazing that millions of years later, another human being dug up the same pebble, recognized the same face, and maybe even, for a moment, dreamed the same dreams. You stepped on a human being back there.

That's - um, that's beautiful too?

today is the day i write a comic where dinosaurs refer to humans as evolving in their past

ah, the dream of being a jerk while having a doctor's note saying it's allowed

1314 so i was watching the golden girls on dvd a few years ago at a party (WOO!!! SPRING BREAK) and the pilot episode goes to great lengths to explain that Sophia's rudeness throughout the series was the result of a stroke. it was like the midichlorians from star wars, but they actually WERE in the first episode produced. so anyway, the take-away here is that george lucas ripped off golden girls

it turns out i basically already wrote yesterday's comic on December 11th 2006! but you can read yesterday's comic as a sequel to that, only with utahraptor being all "t-rex you can never win with me, my friend"

everyone, think of how much fun things would be if we used "fubs" instead of "um"! police would be all, "where were you the night of april 21st, son?" and we'd be all, "fubs, uh, fubs..."

MY BROTHER TOLD ME THIS JOKE OVER THE PHONE AND THEN WE WORKED TOGETHER TO RECONSTRUCT HOW FUNNY IT MUST HAVE BEEN BEFORE HE HEARD IT

It is common to imagine your life as a story, with yourself as the main character! It's a story with no real climax that always ends with you totally dead.

However!

My issue is that STUFF happens to main characters: dramatic stuff! Stuff that's not always good. It would be fun to be a bit character, a guy who gets one or two lines and whose personality is encapsulated in a few words: 'likes boats', 'old and wise', or 'eats a lot and, therefore, can't control himself around food. When someone says "Where's the beef?" he runs up and says, "Did someone say BEEF?" because that is definitely how people who like food act.'

Then I was thinking, maybe I am that!

But you've said WAY more than two lines, my friend!

Yeah, but it's Rosencrantz and Guildenstern, right? I've got my own life, but it only counts when I'm around the main character. Everything else is forgotten!

So who's the main character?

...Dromiceio-mimus?

MUCH LATER, OUTSIDE DROMICEIOMIMUS' HOUSE.

Dromiceiomimus! Are you in?

T-Rex?! What are you doing here? It's late! It's 3 AM!

I - like boats?

that "likes food" background character guy? he's me. i know the day i hear someone within earshot, but still far enough away that i'd have to run up to them to talk, actually say "where's the beef?": this is my moment. this is my line. this is how i will be remembered. "...Did someone say BEEF??"

HAHA I SHOUTED IT AFTER SOMEONE WHO WAS RUNNING

people in relationships: you're no better! excepting your current one, every single relationship YOU'VE ever had has been so unsuccessful it's ended in breakups too. unless you're this really successful polyamorist, in which case, well, YOU can excuse yourself from the room while the rest of us feel bad and stare at our shoes.

"FRIENDSHIP IN MOTION"

1329

I BLAME HIM FOR THIS PATENTLY RIDICULOUS SITUATION

1330

mathematicians in the audience are just getting more and more pissed

who told you i was racist? was it... a minority?

i couldn't find any other reference for "frigedun" except for wikipedia, so wikipedia, you better not let me down on this one, i swear to god

1334

it's true, gentle reader! in a better world, you're looking forward to Casual Frigday

Whenever I think of the phrase "good to the last drop" I think of friggin' Maxwell House Coffee.

I don't even drink coffee!

They have lexicalized the phrase AND associated it in my mind with their stupid branding!

And if someone says "can't get enough of that Sugar Crisp" NOT ONLY do I think of Sugar Crisp, I think of the jingle too!

Oh, actually, about that: they're rebranding it, T-Rex. It's now referred to as "Golden Crisp" in most major markets.

WHAT? They stored a phrase in my sparkling mind and now they're abandoning it? I call FRIGGIN' SHENANIGANS on that!

So what are you going to do?

Um, refer to it as "Sugar Crisp" till the day I die??

Except THEN I'll just be reinforcing their original branding. Okay, tell you what: I can't forget the slogans but I CAN substitute their brands with something I do want to remember, like intercourse!

"Can't get enough of that intercourse"?

Exactly!

"Silly rabbit! Intercourse is for kids." Wow!

That idea backfired incredibly quickly!

You've got questions. We've got intercourse.

1336

hey, remember how I couldn't go out hallowe'en 2008 because i had that creepy date with my neighbours? i do. i still do.

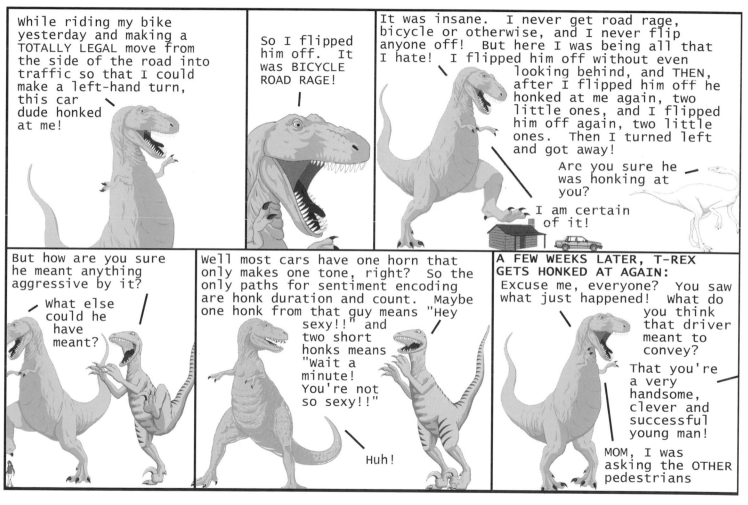

While riding my bike yesterday and making a TOTALLY LEGAL move from the side of the road into traffic so that I could make a left-hand turn, this car dude honked at me!

So I flipped him off. It was BICYCLE ROAD RAGE!

It was insane. I never get road rage, bicycle or otherwise, and I never flip anyone off! But here I was being all that I hate! I flipped him off without even looking behind, and THEN, after I flipped him off he honked at me again, two little ones, and I flipped him off again, two little ones. Then I turned left and got away!

Are you sure he was honking at you?

I am certain of it!

But how are you sure he meant anything aggressive by it?

What else could he have meant?

Well most cars have one horn that only makes one tone, right? So the only paths for sentiment encoding are honk duration and count. Maybe one honk from that guy means "Hey sexy!!" and two short honks means "Wait a minute! You're not so sexy!!"

Huh!

A FEW WEEKS LATER, T-REX GETS HONKED AT AGAIN:

Excuse me, everyone? You saw what just happened! What do you think that driver meant to convey?

That you're a very handsome, clever and successful young man!

MOM, I was asking the OTHER pedestrians

in morse code, he was saying "t" "i"

it is probably the hardest to defend against.

How great would it be to be able to make your voice sound like somebody else's?

SUPER GREAT??

Probably! Because then I could do prank calls as you, Dromiceiomimus! I could call Utahraptor as you and invite him over for dinner, and then, when he shows up for dinner, you're liable to be unprepared for company!

Possibly! Or, I could be prepared and we could have a great time without you.

I- um.

OKAY, as revenge for that, I could prank call Dromiceiomimus and pretend that I'm a celebrity she likes!

It won't work!

We all know about your plans now! If you ever do develop voice talent, we'll all be totally prepared for your little prank calls.

Well, I'VE actually got an emergency SUPER SECRET prank that I won't talk about, in case I ever do get the chance to pull it off.

HEY, LET'S ALL READ T-REX'S THOUGHTS!

Man, if I don't find a washroom soon others will be disappointed in me

HUH.

I REALLY THOUGHT HE'D BE THINKING ABOUT HIS SUPER SECRET PRANK

it's to call up utahraptor and say "hello this is utahraptor, who is this?" in a very stern utahraptor voice. it's better on paper.

1340

The ultimatum game is an economics game thing! Two anonymous strangers have to decide how to divide a sum of money between themselves.

Player One proposes a non-zero split, and Player Two can either accept or reject it!

If Two accepts, they both take their money and go their separate ways. But if Two rejects, NOBODY gets any money. And the game is played only once, so there's no worry about reprisals.

So what's the problem? Player Two should accept all the time - some money is better than none, right?

That's what's so interesting! When there's really unfair offers (90/10, 99/1), some players reject them anyway.

Maybe they'd rather have their pride than a few dollars!

Exactly!

I suppose it shows that people aren't motivated ENTIRELY by greed, even in situations involving money and a stranger you'll never see again.

Exactly, and that's something! We're not ALL motivated by greed. Some of us are ALSO motivated by pride.

"VICTORIES WHERE WE CAN TAKE THEM"

on the other hand, in smaller cultures with a greater focus on community, player one often makes a very generous offer! so if you're all :(after this comic at least now you can be all :l

the serial numbers are included in the comic because this way you'll know if you found the right one!

TRUE FACTS: i can think of no great painting that can be described as "the one where the woman is - surfing?" THE BIRTH OF VENUS DOESN'T COUNT SHE'S JUST SORT OF STANDING THERE AND THERE'S NOT EVEN ANY WICKED WAVES

1345   the "cake-cutting problem" is a well-known mathematical problem! i would argue that the world would be AT LEAST 5% BETTERER had the nomenclature gone differently and mathematicians had spent the 20th century discussing the hilariously-named cheese-cutting problem instead

Today is the day I find I'm no longer immersed in popular culture. I used to be SUBMERGED in it, but now I'm not even in the lake! I'm on the shore, dripping wet, furrowing my brow and pointing at the lake in confusion.

Today is the day I realize saying something "rocks" is actually really weird!

It's like a switch went off in my head. This radio station was all bragging on itself, saying "Kewl 105: WE ROCK!" and my first thought was, "Like a moored boat? Is it cool now to sway back and forth, like a boat tied to a dock by a length of rope?"

You're taking it literally?

That's the thing! My FIRST INSTICT was to take it literally. I had to remind myself what they really meant.

Then I thought of "rock concerts" and it seemed silly! But "punk rock" seemed ADORABLE.

You just need to ROCK MORE!

I know you're trying Utahraptor, but it really sounds like you're saying I should pitch dangerously to one side a little more often. It's too late for me. Tell them my story.

Goodbye, T-Rex. We had a good run, didn't we?

We did. By God, we did.

Hey, when I decide that "cool" can only mean that something's chilly, you'll still shoot me with the kryptonite bullet, right?

No worries!

Awesome!

Awesome

i used to be SUBMERGED in it, but now i'm not even in the lake! i'm on the shore, dripping wet, coughing up blood.

1346

if someone was spying on me this morning, they would have seen a man get out of bed, have a shower, get dressed, and then write a made up story about flying dinosaurs and vaginas while listening to the official soundtrack of the game "super mario galaxy". they would have thought "i must remind myself again why i am spying on this fellow"

"EUPHEMISMS" FOR DATING

Yes! Maybe sometimes you don't want to throw the fact that you've found happiness in the arms of another in my face? Maybe you need some "euphemisms".

For example!

Instead of saying "Sally and I are now dating exclusively" you can say "Sally and I are now seeing other people ONLY WITH REGRET." On second thought, maybe you should keep the "Sally and I are now dating exclusively" because if I don't want to acknowledge your commitment, I can play dumb and say, "Sally and you are now dating exclusively... axe murderers? Mad scientists? Um, DOGS?"

So, hey, your euphemisms are pretty weak so far!

Yes. Allow me to correct that!

Instead of "T-Rex, we're dating": "T-Rex, we're eating an awful lot of picnics on Sundays", "T-Rex, we're hanging out more than can be politely explained away", "T-Rex, we're playing Mega Man in two-player mode".

Mega Man doesn't have a two-player mode.

Not for us, Utahraptor! Not for us.

sigh

sorry, mad scientists, i didn't mean to imply you were undateable. the more i think about it, the more i'm convinced: you probably set up some pretty awesome dates.

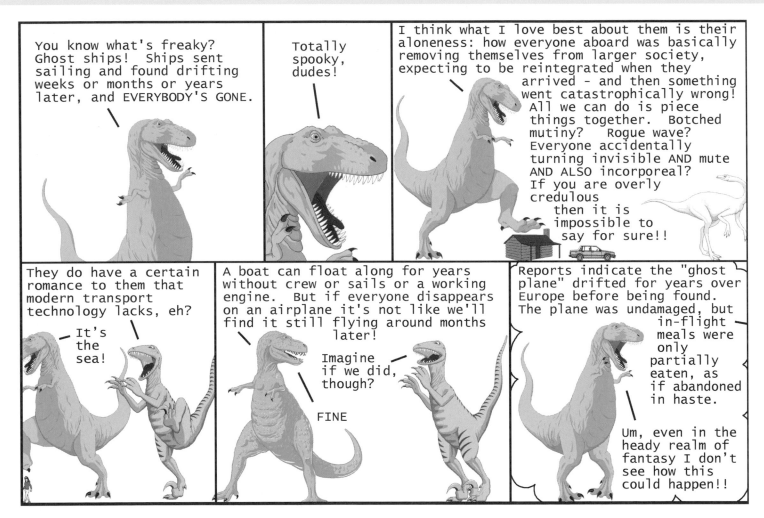

the secret is not to dwell

1353

oh word 97, why do you not have "macbeth" in your spell check dictionary? you have had between 402 and 405 years to get your head in the game here.

1355

LATER: aliens discover midas's body and use him as a highly unstable source of gold, keeping him in vacuum suspension with magnetic fields. but their ship soon suffers a power failure, midas hits the floor, and the ship is transmuted. the ship drifts until drawn in by the gravitational field of a backwater planet, where it crashes and causes the planet to suffer the same fate as Earth. we join our story centuries later as our heroes, bounty hunters seeking the near-mythic Midas Flesh, successfully break quarantine and get past the defences erected around the planet. they are the first to land on the Second Golden Planet.

i hesitate to release the idea of preemptive plagiarism onto the internet, lest it be discovered that it has been preemptively plagiarized! :0

Oh my goodness I just figured out what I was meant to do with my life. I have discovered my CALLING.

Body farm owner!!

Forensic anthropologists want to study how bodies decompose in different circumstances! And so they go to their neighbourhood BODY FARM, which is basically just a few acres of land surrounded by a fence and filled with DEAD AND DECOMPOSING BODIES. Some are out in the open, others are underwater or entombed or whatever! And scientists come and science up the joint, and I'LL get to be the guy who holds a torch under his face and says "Welcome to my farm of death and decay."

I'd only say that sometimes, Utahraptor.

You'd only say it never!

There are tons of legal, ethical, and security issues you're not even considering!

"Security issues"! What's better security than living in a house surrounded by CORPSES? "Oh hey, let's go steal the TV from the corpse house"? NOBODY HAS EVER SAID THAT, UTAHRAPTOR!!

Honestly, Utahraptor. If you keep being so down on my body farm idea, when you die I might not let you decay out in the open on my front lawn!

T-Rex, what I am about to say, I say with all honesty.

In my heart of hearts, I truly thought we already had such an accord

welcome to my farm of death and decay BOILS AND GHOULS, of CORPSE we're open 24 hours, to enter the body farm you'll need to enter your password which is protected by 256-bit enCRYPTion, etc

YOU GUYS!! IT DOESN'T EVEN SOUND THAT FUN BUT IT STILL MANAGES TO DISAPPOINT

pascal just wasn't thinking big enough

I have kissed a lady. I have seen PLENTY of beautiful sunsets. I've even driven a car through a fruit stand during a car chase!

...What's left?

This, my friends, is the malaise of the glutton at life's buffet, The Man Who Achieved Too Much Too Soon. He looks ahead, his life not half over, and sees no more frontiers to conquer, no more challenges, no more surprises! All that remains is a slow slide into compromise and old age, the long December spent waiting for the day his mind and body finally fail.

Then: death!

Hah! We're seriously talking about you here?

Hey, here's some things you've never done! You've never tried fugu, punched out a ghost, gotten married, eaten your way out of a whale, gone heli-skiing, or been shot at by a criminal, but then ran around the bullets at super speed, grabbed the criminal, and then ran back at super speed so that he could be shot by his own bullets.

MEANWHILE, IN THE UNIVERSE WHERE T-REX HAS DONE THESE THINGS:

Well!

I guess I could do them in ORDER...

i realized after writing it that you can read this comic as being prejudiced against disability, seniors, alcoholics, insomniacs, arthritics, people with skin cancer, the suicidal, the diseased and the dead. so um, please don't do that?

and thank YOU, google search for "one in seven canadians"! i had no idea what my seventh friend, BRANDI LEE MACDONALD, was up to

1367

city folk: sheep are awesome because when they say "baaa" it honestly sounds like someone doing a bad sheep impression. when you walk up on a herd of sheep you will think "wow, there are a lot of people making fun of sheep just over the next hill." it's insane!

Panel 1: "T-Rex," she said "I'm in love with you." She gazed into his eyes, smiling. "I thought about it, and it's DEFINITELY because you're so handsome and intelligent."

Panel 2: T-Rex laughed!

Panel 3: "Baby," he replied, "it's also because I am sexy and loveable and smart and manly and sexy." She was nodding. He paused, looked around, and then whispered, "I put 'sexy' in twice because I'm - "
"- twice as sexy" she whispered back, the two of them whispering it together. She knew that he was twice as sexy as a regular sexy man. That was probably a good thing for their relationship, he decided. Better that she know now, than be surprised down the road!

Panel 4: Suddenly she threw up on T-Rex, over and over until he was drenched in digestive fluid!
No! That's not what happened!

Panel 5: Um - "That's not what happened," she said, wiping her mouth. T-Rex realized that it wasn't vomit, it was -
- ultravomit, a new form of vomit that was digesting him alive! As his skin began to dissolve, T-Rex's face melted, slid down the side of his neck, and plopped onto the ground.

Panel 6: FOR SOME REASON T-REX AND UTAHRAPTOR PUBLISH THEIR COLLABORATIVE STORY! IT GOES STRAIGHT TO NUMBER 1
Woo!
WHEN SORTED BY REVERSE POPULARITY
awww daaaang

t-rex blinked, now just an animate skeleton with eyes. "i have always wondered if i would end up as an alive skeleton" he said. he rattled his ribs with his bony knuckles. "it appears that this question is now answered, i guess"

1368

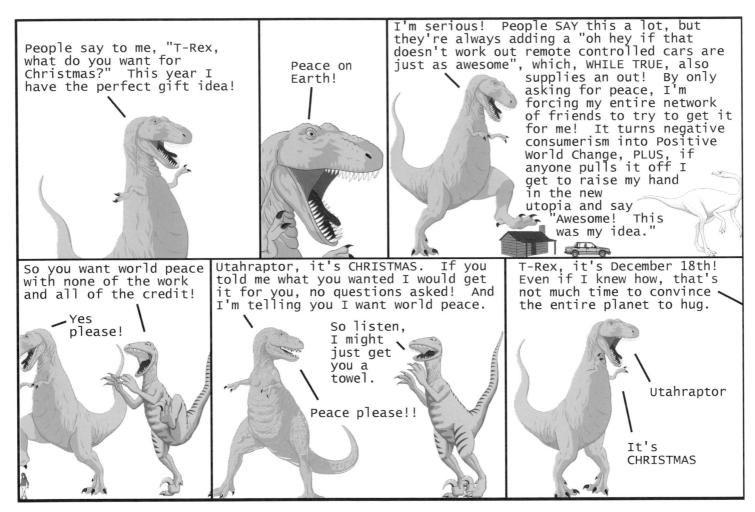

if you were really my friend, you'd appreciate how i manipulate social mores and statutory holidays for gain. gain for everyone?

it's true! wikipidia will cheerfully tell you santa isn't real. here's a question "the media" won't ask:
WHY DOES WIKIPEDIA HATE CHRISTMAS??

now, if you'll excuse me, I'M going to go float in a volume of water.

Indices

Index Alpha: Suggested Email Subject Lines

for when you need to write to me about what you have just read

1168 the moral here is always google your fiancés

1169 ryan i clicked all over this comic but the radio buttons did not change, plz to advise

1170 aw man, panel two, gross

1171 rear-ended the car in front of you? Maybe A Kiss Will Help (TM)

1172 okayokay, the NEW slogan will be "yes. you will die on this treadmill."

1173 thanks for the moral support there, GOD

1174 enemies hear t-rex say that and are all, aw man, i hate that guy

1175 utahraptor thinks happiness and the desire for happiness is tied into a lot of sentient activity. what we need here is experimental proof.

1176 in t-rex's version of the story, he met a bear and the bear was like, man, I DEFINITELY gotta give my props.

1177 the horse does a butt stomp on the Duke of Buckingham, and i know i can now never go back to controlling human protagonists

1178 programming languages make that happen SO OFTEN. they make it happen EVERY THURSDAY AFTERNOON.

1179 it - it would be a big car.

1180 ryan where can i contact a reverse pickpocket? i have so many unwanted and uncooked pieces of rotelle pasta

1181 i wish i could say this betrayal was a LITTLE unexpected, mr. tusks!

1182 vacuum robot directives one and two are concerned with forbidding forbidden vacuuming styles

1183 volcanoes erupt, earthquakes strike, buses drive at unsensible speeds

1184 "nationwide, folks slip on the lube."

1185 inspired by thomas king's "the truth about stories". it's a pretty great book you guys!

1186 "yakety sax", by spider rich and boots randolph: all you need to know is that if you are singularly lucky, you will, at one point in your life, be chased by someone wearing a gorilla suit, and this song will play.

1187 taking the lyrics of every the beach boys song and piecing them together into a giant narrative is lot easier to do with the party-centric stories of andrew w.k.

1188 feelings in his bones said to find a home from the queen of england to the hounds of hell? that doesn't make sense, t-rex. jack white would not cotton to that.

1189 guess what, mom? you're either standing a bit away from me or on speakerphone!

1190 ben's like, "oh yeah? well screw you too, buddy!" and t-rex says "HEY! WE'RE NOT BUDDIES" and it's about as harsh as t-rex gets but then it's only because he really didn't like his movies?

1191 speak for yourself, t-rex. i've spent my 18 years thinking about race cars. they're neat!

1192 ryan is it "ninja teens" or "ninja teams"? either option appears to be contentious

1193 ryan, I assure you: i will be continuing this debate on my blog

1194 the exclamation point is part of the name. it's not "giraffe division", it's "giraffe division!"

1195 stabbin' dudes, havin' broods, watchin' plays that allow murder to be construed

1196 it is a universe with problems for team t-rex

1197 seriously, battery technology! why can't you be more like integrated circut technology?

1198 "If you want to act like me you just need to hold your hands like I do and say "RAR" often, as is my wont."

1199 what he likes, what his interests are, how gay he was and how francis bacon he was - all the stuff historians wish they had!

1200 that smile is one of FRIENDSHIP

1201 hey. that was a lot of text there.

1202 apparently ermeswindis was a dutch woman living before 1100

1203 my question is this: has there been any progress made on clooney tunes

1204 riddle me this: HOW ARE GEORGE CLOONEY AND SEINFELD HANGING OUT IN DINOSAUR TIMES

1205 hi! here's some things that could go wrong today! in bed!

1206 Batman: he's Australian now.

1207 here we've moved beyond the misuse of 'literally' and all the way into 'i sometimes don't get figurative language unless it is clearly denoted and demarked'

1208 QUIT BRIDLIN' YOUR OPTIMISM

1209 YOUTH SOCIETAL EXPECTATIONS OF THE ELDERLY COMICS

1210 panel six, recreating the classic romantic painting, 'dinosaur who maybe needs to go the bathroom'

1211 is t-rex auditioning for a role in a film that dromiceiomimus and utahraptor have already been cast in, or is t-rex actually auditioning for a role in dinosaur comics? it is totally the former.

1212 I've already told you! It's a show about RVs and the vacation adventures one may choose to take in them.

1213 you can tell i'm canadian when my idea of directly telling someone they're wrong is to say "well, maybe there are other options." GEEZ

1214 please to sing these lyrics over the real ones, should they appear at sporting events. you know, for when the senators score a goal, and they play "candle in the wind"

1215 man, anyway, what IS for dinner?

1216 but - what if they did?

1217 this is pre-emptive revenge for that turkey baaaaaa

1218 he means that literally. there's a place called "The Komedy Klub" down the road from a place called "The Comedy Club". there is Competition

1219 i enjoyed programming the parts where you can borrow a strangers's car, and then crash the car, and them come back to the stranger and say 'sorry i crashed your car'.

1220 dreams as signifier is just one of the many narrative tropes that make you go hmmm

1221 if you're STILL having trouble naming your characters, try - try going with their species?

1222 oh, mr. tusks! how do you make puns that only make sense in text work in spoken language?

1223 that's genetic! utahraptor! plus we're dinosaurs and none of us have hair!!

1224 patient complains of ankle pain. hairline fracture found in middle cuneiform. patient has self-diagnosed a desire for being given the news, and believes himself to have a bad case of loving me.

1225 soap operas also don't reboot continuity when they want a divorce to happen OH SNAP

1226 hey! looks like someone else has "do it because it'll make such a great story" disease too

1227 IF YOU MUST KNOW, LIBRARIAN, I PLAN TO READ THE HORSE BOOK WHILE GLANCING UP AT PICTURES OF TRAINS AND SIGHING. MY RELATIONSHIP WITH MY FRIEND UTAHRAPTOR IS - COMPLICATED

1228 ryan is dromi describing a complete directed edge-weighted graph with the friends as nodes, and the quality of each friend's relationship to her to divided by physical distance between the two nodes as the weight, so then it's just the NP-hard problem of finding the most expensive (rather than cheapest) traversal starting with from her position??

1229 my friend chip knows the exact amount of money at which it is not worth his time to fish it out of a used toilet. that value is $20.

1230 IMMOGBNR ;)

1231 sounds like a good date!!

1232 ryan what do you think happens in battlestar galactica next week? feelings and explosions?

1233 let's learn SCIENCE

1267 my friends, i ask the boldest question. it is about He Who Should Not Be Named Unless You Want Folks To Think You're A Sucky Greek.

1268 precisely the reason i don't wear pants these days

1269 t-rex needs to lay off reading the teen magazeens. nobody above 16 says "current crush"! plus, come on t-rex,creepy.

1270 is it capers that may be taking years off my life? capers? this is the first time I've had them. normally they're used only as a garnish, but ah, I like 'em alright

1271 t-rex why are you pointing out that paul grice is dead now. we all know it

1272 paul grice: still dead :(

1273 later, t-rex remembers that he's already invented like 10 super heroes, and writes some stories in which the transformer guy and super lee and spoiler alert "team up"! CONTINUITY

1274 i hate all conspiracy theories except for the ones that involve time travel. the selective skepticism and eagerness to believe is projected onto something totally absurd and awesome! ANYONE WHO TELLS YOU TIME TRAVEL ISN'T POSSIBLE IS A TIME TRAVELLER WITH SOMETHING TO HIDE

1275 being a bear aggravator is okay. the work is fine, but you start to wonder who's writing the paycheques, you know?

1276 a small case of the chubbs: good porn movie title, or best porn movie title?

1277 afterwards, macgregor tried to pull the same scam again in france and then AGAIN in england. he combines "loveable scamp" with "total dick and psychopathic murderer"!

1278 wow, SOMEBODY here believes that pointed awards ceremony features heavily in the afterlife

1279 "i'm almost certain you added the emphasis to the medias res definition, utahraptor. ninty-nine percent"

1280 the deal with method 3 is that your sweetie is like, "man, i can't be with someone who does such terrible accents. i can't tell if the accent is racist or just terrible. can it be both? i'll think about this after we're broken up, i guess."

1281 ryan one time i was single and i was like "man, SCREW THIS" so this comic works out well

1282 t-rex is from the old "analogies as perfect 1:1 correspondences" skool. it's a good skool to be in for the purposes of debate?

1283 t-rex was kind of a dick in the past there. i'm with boorishly. boorishly is a pretty great name.

1284 ryan i was going to email you to complain about the cussin' but then i read panel 2 and saw you agreed with me. sweet.

1285 ryan this is why i always schedule my dates on inappropriately lusty day. i get to make out and whisper, "don't you find this deliciously... /inappropriate/?"

1286 when utahraptor really starts to party he parties like a rock star NAMED marty in the year 1999.

1287 what you have to imagine is t-rex lying in bed with an accounting book in his hands and he's reading it and, quietly, saying "weeeeeeeeee"

1288 i suspect it has something - SOMETHING - to do with boners.

1289 SPEAKERPHONE I LOVE HOW I CAN USE YOU FROM ACROSS THE ROOM

1290 in the 50s, we all agreed to design robots like they were awesome. then in the 90s we all RENEGED ON OUR AGREEMENT and came up with these inoffensive shiny friendly boxes. i think maybe our grandparents had the right idea?

1291 also, t-rex, it's a comic where you have no dialogue, just text captions explaining over and over what's going on in the pictures. that's - that's a concern

1292 oh monocle guy, if only monocles popping out in surprise wasn't so dang satisfying

1293 "A third store was giving out free pamphlets about the store, but that one was less exciting. I was mostly calling about the first one."

1294 ryan my roommates are annoying BUT they don't leave their socks in the cereal. should i change the comic or should i just wait until they do

1295 ryan i can read the last panel as a close up on t-rex's body or i can read it as saying that in the future, shit's green. sorry for the swearing but can you tell me which one is correct

1296 this is an old idea, but i played bingo last night for the first time in years and felt more unnecessary to the whole process than ever. now when you win, they don't even call out the winning numbers for verification! they call out the SERIAL NUMBER on the card, and the computer verifies that it's a winner. the whole process made me feel bizarrely patronized by the machines involved, wishing they'd just replace me with themselves already.

1297 god's like, "WHAT? THAT'S NOT HOW YOU PLAY BINGO. IT'S NO BIGGIE, THOUGH, IT JUST SURPRISED ME A LITTLE. ANYWAY. GO NUTS"

1298 things like the burgess shale fauna basically define "awesome and surreal", but t-rex is talking about butt hands here. you must concede that we are dealing with a new category.

1299 ryan i was going to email you to say "FOUR feet? don't you mean TWO FEET and TWO HANDS" but then i thought maybe having four feet could be just a small part of what makes the day so memorable!

1300 next up: utahraptor gives t-rex forms to change his name to "t-rexe", the passionate, painterly frenchman

1301 what t-rex was going to say was "and I'VE had enough of those to last a month of sundays"

1302 is it a very polite member of the staff, or is it marcie from peanuts

1303 i just file what i THINK my taxes should be, and if the government wants to audit me, they can go ahead! audits are like getting a very motivated accountant that figures out all your tax stuff FOR FREE.

1304 ryan, utahraptor doesn't think all artists want to be number one, but he thinks it would be interesting to see how some of them react when it's no longer a possibility. just - thought i'd let you know?

1305 sometimes i worry i wouldn't want to be friends with me. sometimes i'm proud of it.

1306 please to explain more this intriguing notion of "physical friendship"

1307 it is my understanding that there are similar issues with harry potter and time-turner backers

1308 RIP CHARLES OSBORNE. YOU HAD THE HICCUPS FOR 68 YEARS AND THEY STARTED WHEN YOU SLAUGHTERED A PIG. I DON'T KNOW MUCH ELSE ABOUT YOU.

1309 I didn't realize I was missing out at weddings until I heard about this stereotype.

1310 it's - it's self-diagnosed

1311 THIS IS THE LAST TIME I PROMISE A GAME OF MADLIBS TO EVERY SENTIENT BEING I'M TOTALLY SERIOUS

1312 utahraptor and dromiceiomimus are getting PRETTY GOOD at figuring out what's going on from only one half of a conversation

1313 archeologists are like "maybe an animal ate this shell and then pooped it out, GROSS" and then the other archelogists are like, "eww, you touched it!!"

1314 you'd also be unable to walk in the dark! or, for that matter, walk without staring at your feet. good times?

1315 a level five reverse godwin with perfect dismount

1316 it - it wasn't fubs who peed on the couch.

1317 it's still a confusing joke. i just, well, i just don't see how it could happen in real life.

1318 listen, dromiceiomimus, what do you need from me? let

me know what kind of main character you are, so i know what kind of background character to be.

1319 utahraptor forgot to mention "sustainable", so if t-rex comes up with an energy source that matches all his other adjectives, he's gonna have to decide whether or not to tell him "it's still not enough."

1320 no matter how bad life gets, i can always say, 'well, i mean, at least i'm not shouting "run forrest, run!" after someone.'

1321 what is it they say on battlestar galactica? "frap"? i forget these things when they don't make a new episode for SIX MONTHS

1322 i was going to make fun of those pointless "which console was better/top 10 consoles evar" arguments online, but then i was like, well, it's CLEARLY the snes. even the devil came around once he actually got to try one.

1323 in panel 4, t-rex is saying 'one got tired' to refer to his feet. BUT, he could also be saying 'one got tired' to refer to himself in the past tense! what a guy

1324 would that my friendships could end in such decisive and memorable ways

1325 i for one think john has lovingly rendered dromiceiomimus' legs, and that his affection for her shows clearly through them

1326 t-rex's expression in panel four mirrors my own when i examine my changing body in the mirror

1327 yesterday i said t-rex's expression mirrors my own when i examine my changing body in the mirror but i totally mean it today for panel six! i look at it and it's like, wow, that's How I Start My Mornings

1328 this is called the droste effect! how many special effects are named after brands of cocoa from the netherlands? to my knowledge, this effect is PROBABLY among the first

1329 the new ds is gonna have slightly bigger screens and a CAMERA

1330 i have the vigilante gene. it makes me wish my name was actually "vigilante gene".

1331 when you're underwater, nobody can tell you're crying. oh, aquaman.

1332 i have had cupcakes made by an Actual Racist and ANYWAY they tasted like delicioius oranges and now i know the taste of prejudice

1333 are t-rex's four fingers nicknamed "the few"

1334 in an alternate universe i'm studying frigg on the shore of the batman river, on the edge of batman city, the lovely capital of batman province, turkey! man. kinda sucks the joy out of actuarial science

1335 ryan are you the first to modify the anthropic principle to individuals and alternate timelines? if so, i propose this be called the "individualistic anthropic principle of 'things are pretty okay for me i guess'"

1336 can't get enough of that Mom's Birthday on August 16th!

1337 IN ORDER TO COMPLETE THIS COSTUME, I HAD TO PUT MAKEUP OVER ALL THE HORRIBLE PHYSICAL SCARS I GOT IN THE INTERVENING YEARS

1338 q: how does t-rex flip someone off with only two fingers? a: with ENTHUSAISM.

1339 utahraptor raises roofs AND levels of debates

1340 holy crap, i have to go to the washroom. holy crap, i may lose esteem in the eyes of my peers.

1341 ECONOMICS, huh??

1342 i mistyped "christmas" as "christman" and thought "hilarious! he can be a superhero of christmas!" but then i was all "oh wait nevermind i have just invented christianity"

1343 ripped from the headlines of today ripped from the headlines of thirty years ago

1344 people from ottawa: you can add "voice of fire" to the list

1345 ryan you could have said "heck gosh, it's strawberry cake", and heck gosh, why did you not

1346 "rock me amadeus" now only sounds like an irish

stereotype demanding that his amadeus be swayed

1347 you try to be a good friend, but then you find out your friends lock their doors

1348 utahraptor, we ALREADY AGREED: Symbolism is Boring, Dreams are Awesome.

1349 t-rex is being ridiculous. he should be more trusting of giant corporations that literally profit off of death.

1350 YOU GOT: RELATIONSHIP

1351 it was as if all the passengers had just stepped out of their seats for a quick cigarette, never to return, which is impossible, since smoking is not allowed on these flights.

1352 somehow i expected more from a recordkeeping organization founded on a whim by a beer company

1353 racists are great because you can be racist against them and then the only people who get mad at you are racists!

1354 i don't know why people find deus ex machina unsatisfying. what's not to like in james bond being in a sticky wicket, and then GOD HIMSELF shows up and squishes the heads of the bad guys, and then james bond whispers, "sweet"?

1355 ryan what if aliens divided up the Midas Flesh with lasers into six pieces (torso, four limbs, and head) and distributed it across the galaxy for safe keeping. but one keeper if the Flesh is tempted! alarms go off and they find his body, a gold statue with an empty hand where the Midas Skull should be. the chase is on to track down the most dangerous weapon in the universe!!

1356 Attention, people who are breaking up with someone, and took some time out right in the middle of THAT conversation to read comics on the internet. Here's an incredibly useful comic for you right now!!

1357 "vow 43: if i ever meet the ghost of Nicolas Fatio de Duillier i will ask him why he got his idea discredited before i got even the chance. this i swear."

1358 ryan i just read a comic about an idea for a comic so

here is an email about an idea for an email

1359 in real life, as near as i can tell, there's no house that you can live in situated in the middle of these body farms. SOMETIMES LIFE IS A LITANY OF DISAPPOINTMENT

1360 apparently in the last panel t-rex is attending - nursery school?

1361 t-rex's estimation of the number of religions varies wildly each panel, is this by design

1362 the criminal's last words would be "wow, that was kind of a dick move"

1363 this comic takes place in an alternate universe in which canada exists

1364 the nice thing about vampires is that if someone says "no that's not how vampires work" you can say "yes it is", and then, nobody is right

1365 my question is, what do the ants that combined themselves into the shape of a giant ant think of this

1366 gentlemen: a recent discovery has rocked our understanding of our past and our origins. by chance or by design, it falls upon my shoulders to deliver to you now this momentous sentence: history is ruined, you guys.

1367 it's due to the cephalopods! sheep have OCTOPUS EYES

1368 i am entirely charmed by the idea of someone throwing up and saying "that's not what happened" as they wipe their mouth. it's ultimate faith in the power of language!

1369 the script for this comic called for utahraptor to say "So you want world peace with none of the work and all of the credit!" and t-rex to say "Yes please!" and then to step on a tiny woman to death

1370 utahraptor is old-school classy. he gets emailed a link like that, and he thinks, "yes, this is something that deserves an in-person response."

1371 wikipedia is alive and you can kiss wikipedia now. some of us may find this concept - distracting?

1372 they are still putting daffy duck on baseball caps too. yep.

Index Omega: An Actual Index For You to Use

Guest Comics

While writing this book, I asked some cartoonist friends to create their own Dinosaur Comics. They turned out **TOTALLY RAD**.

THE THUNDER-LIZARD'S
Day Out

STARRING
THOS. REX, ESQ.

The morning dawned bright and clear as the thunder-lizard began his perambulation.

The neighbour-woman was outside tending her radishes. "Good morning," said the thunder-lizard. "Good morning!" said the neighbour-woman, a different (and inferiour) species of thunder-lizard.

"I'm so glad you've come by," she said. "I ordered this hat from the specialty thunder-lizard haberdashery, but it's the wrong size! It looks like it might fit you, though—would you care for it?"

"*Would* I!" beamed the thunder-lizard. What a morning!

"Ho, there," came a cry from across the boulevard. "Quite a smashing hat you've got there!" It was the thunder-lizard's friend, another thunder-lizard.

"It's the latest in fashions for thunder-lizards," said the thunder-lizard. "It fits my crown perfectly!" "Ah, but can it withstand a scissor-kick to the noggin?" asked the friend. "I've just come from judo class and I'm eager to share what I've learnt." The idiotic nature of this idea went unnoticed by either party.

Twenty seconds later, the longstanding friendship was over.

NON-CANON

by John Campbell
pictent.com

by Randall Munroe
xkcd.com

by Anthony Clark
nedroid.com

by Kate Beaton
harkavagrant.com

Ryan North is the author of all these comics you just read, and then some! He posts new Dinosaur Comics each day to qwantz.com from his house in sunny Toronto, Canada. But what's going on in these pictures? He doesn't even like pancakes that much; what the heck??

COMICS THAT SMELL *PERFECTLY FINE*

THREE WORD PHRASE
by **Ryan Pequin**

These are some comics that Ryan Pequin drew. Some of them he drew with a pencil but most of them he drew on the computer. If you enjoy jokes about birds that are the president, bears who have extremely low self-esteem, or how nobody likes you, then you should probably just go ahead and buy this thing.

books: **topatoco.com/threewordphrase**
read online: **threewordphrase.com**

NEDROID PICTURE DIARY
by **Anthony Clark**

Beartato is a bear who is also a potato. His best friend is a bird-man. Sometimes there is a walking shark or a mean dog. Don't worry! This is almost entirely made-up.

books: **topatoco.com/nedroid**
read online: **nedroid.com**

AMAZINGSUPERPOWERS
by **Wes & Tony**

A comic written in blood and bound in human flesh. A blood called "jokes" and a human flesh called "you chuckling your cute little tucus off." Enjoy 180+ full-color comics, not to mention 14+ pages of never-before-seen bonus crap that will make your teeth fall out and send you rocketing through puberty all over again.

books: **topatoco.com/goldeneyecheatcodes**
read online: **amazingsuperpowers.com**

HOMESTUCK
by **Andrew Hussie**

The hugely popular and also hugely huge web series, made FOR the web, OF the web, and totally inextricable FROM the web—now in book form!!! It is about some kids who use the Internet a lot and play a magical game that destroys the world. They engage in a high volume of sassy online banter, botch simple tasks frequently, and sometimes accomplish objectives.

books: **topatoco.com/mspa**
read online: **mspaintadventures.com**

A SOFTER WORLD
by **Joey Comeau & Emily Horne**

A Softer World comics are like a weird sad clown that lives under your bed. Except the tears are blood. And when the clown coughs, the most adorable kitten in the world pops out of his mouth and loves you.

books: **topatoco.com/asofterworld**
read online: **asofterworld.com**

WONDERMARK
by **David Malki !**

A sarcastic, silly, and razor-sharp gag comic strip created entirely from 19th-Century woodcuts, this Eisner-, Harvey-, and Ignatz-nominated comic is in equal measures strange, attractive, clever and good-natured—just like you.

books: **topatoco.com/wondermark**
read online: **wondermark.com**

WHOA, imagine if there were more comics you could read?

IMAGINE NO LONGER BECAUSE HERE COMES REALITY:

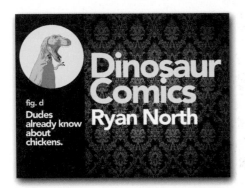

Dudes Already Know About Chickens

256 pages! It's great!

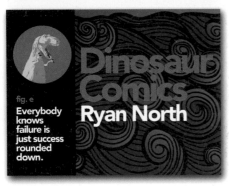

Everybody Knows Failure Is Just Success Rounded Down

256 *more* pages! Even better!

Nice!

a good place to look for these items MIGHT BE topatoco.com/qwantz